ESS

FOLK
TALES

ESSEX
FOLK
TALES

JAN WILLIAMS

The
History
Press

First published 2012

The History Press
The Mill, Brimscombe Port
Stroud, Gloucestershire, GL5 2QG
www.thehistorypress.co.uk

British Library Cataloguing in Publication Data.
A catalogue record for this book is available from the British Library.

ISBN 978 0 7524 6600 2

Typesetting and origination by The History Press
Printed and bound by TJ Books Limited, Padstow, Cornwall

CONTENTS

ACKNOWLEDGEMENTS

I would like to recognise the hard work of Essex local historians and societies in preserving folk tales – thank you to Douglas Carter of Boxford; Peter Gant at the Manningtree Society; Phyl Hendry of St Osyth; Keith Lovell of Tollesbury; the Thaxted Society; the Mersea Museum; the Leigh-on-Sea Society; the Harwich Society; Barbara Tricker of Great Bentley; Winifred Beaumont of Wormingford; and Margaret Leather of Rowhedge. I was introduced to Essex folk songs by Adrian May and his group Potiphar's Apprentices.

There is a huge pleasure in telling stories in good company and I would like to acknowledge the inspiration and companionship of the Essex Storytellers, who originally included Peter Maskens and Carl Merry. After Peter's death, we were joined by Andy Jennings. With this combination of talents, we were able to secure funding for the storytelling production of the tale of Byrhtnoth from Maldon District Council, the story of the Mersea Barrow in the production 'Scratching the Surface' from Arts Council East, and the tales of the witches of Manningtree in the production 'Green Mist Rising' from Heritage Lottery. This sponsorship made it possible to bring our stories to audiences all over the county, and to research and develop them in considerable depth.

I would like to thank Barbara Maskens for the inclusion of her husband Peter's story 'The Last Mountain in Essex', Carl Merry for his retelling of 'The Heart of Thorns' and Andy Jennings for his description of the Roman centurion crossing the Strood.

I would also like to thank the staff of the local studies library in Colchester, Saffron Walden Library, and especially my local library, Brightlingsea, for their long-suffering help in tracking down obscure books.

Finally, I would like to express my appreciation for the help and support of Sylvia Kent, Malcolm Burgess and Alison Barnes. I am especially appreciative of Margaret Hawkins' editorial skills, and Val Johnson and Peter Fowler for their patient encouragement and useful comments.

ILLUSTRATIONS

The striking cover design is by Katherine Soutar and is based on the dramatic story of 'The Poacher and the Mawkin'. The illustration captures the drama of one of the county's darkest tales.

The delightful lino cut prints are the work of talented Brightlingsea artist Simon Peecock. It's been a pleasure to tap into his inventiveness and lively sense of humour.

The other illustrations are listed below:

Foreword

Essex is a place of dark secrets and haunting tales. It is a romantic county for those who have the determination to plunge into its rural heart. It has taken me thirty-five years of living in one of Essex's most beguiling villages, Brightlingsea, to really explore both the county's landscape and its heritage. I am still discovering treasures.

A glance at the map shows that the county's most obvious feature is the ninety miles of coastline facing the North Sea, indented with creeks, navigable rivers and backwaters. Down these waters have come Romans, Anglo-Saxons, Vikings and Normans to plunder and pillage and eventually settle. Boudicca, Byrhtnoth and Haesten all put up a brave fight here and inspired tales of epic proportions. Later, these very same creeks were to be the inspiration for the wildly inventive tales of smugglers determined to hide their booty. Their usual weapon was a rattling good ghost tale to keep the curious at bay.

Strangely enough, it is the mud of the salt marshes which has provided the most dramatic backdrop to Essex stories. The great storyteller Charles Dickens said of Essex that 'all about was stagnation and mud', yet it was a landscape that inspired some of his most evocative writing. Similarly, Sabine Baring-Gould found that his ten years 'on the mud' of Mersea Island may not have been the happiest time of his life, yet in his novel *Mehalah* he wrote the most poetic description of the landscape:

> A more desolate region can scarcely be conceived and yet it is not without beauty. In summer the thrift mantles the marshes with shot satin, passing through all graduations of tint from maiden's blush to lily white. Thereafter a purple glow steals over the waste as the sea lavender bursts into flowers and simultaneously every creek and pool is royally fringed with sea aster. A little later the glasswort, that shot up green and transparent as emerald glass in the early spring, turns to every tinge of carmine. When all vegetation ceases to live and goes to sleep, the marshes are alive and wakeful with countless wild fowl.

The people who lived in the haunting landscape of the marshes often felt so isolated that their dreams were full of alarming shadows. These shadows developed into the weirdest stories. In these tales even the Devil makes his presence felt, and alarming black dogs and knowing cats prowl down country lanes. Ghosts are everywhere. In fact, the paranormal enthusiasts are kept busy with all manner of sightings all over the county. The ghosts' favourite haunt seems to be the Redoubt Fort at Harwich, whose echoing corridors, built in Napoleonic times, have a special magic. If you stop at any ruin or picturesque pub in Essex you will invariably stumble across the well-worn tale of a haunting.

Some of the best tales were collected by the journalist James Wentworth Day. As a keen wild fowler, he met some wonderfully eccentric characters with grand tales to tell. It is through his books that I learnt about the Roman centurion crossing the Strood on Mersea Island, the Viking chief who lost his ships at Benfleet and the ostler who disappeared up the chimney of a well-known inn.

There is also another Essex, depicted on countless chocolate boxes and table mats. Constable painted Essex as much as he painted Suffolk and it is here, in central and north-west Essex, that you find the loveliest villages and richest agricultural lands. There are acres of wonderful wheat, thatched cottages, duck ponds and striking towered churches. Inevitably these make wonderful settings for romances. Did you know, for instance, that Maid Marian was an Essex girl? I suspect that you will at least have heard the story of the Dunmow Flitch, where a flitch of ham is awarded to a married couple who can live without quarrelling for a year and a day. Even today couples compete for it.

Essex's churches are not just impressive architecturally, they are also steeped in history and legend. Thaxted must be among the most glorious churches in England, with one of the most colourful vicars of all. I have found Essex vicars an invaluable source for tales. In fact, the most solid work on Essex's history was done by an eighteenth-century clergyman, Philip Morant, who also wrote *The History and Antiquities of Colchester*. In his day, he cut a picturesque figure with his powdered wig and golden cane, tapping his way as he searched for Roman urns, jewels and coins in the fields around Colchester. The nineteenth-century clergyman Philip Benton had a vast knowledge of wildlife and agricultural land. In his *History of the Rochford Hundred* he could not resist rambling into many folk tales, which are the base of several stories we tell today.

He would have known that agriculture has never been an easy way to make a living, with the constant fear of crops withering and livestock perishing. Out of these deep-rooted anxieties came Essex's blackest stories of all. These were the fearsome accusations of witchcraft that seemed to lurk everywhere. In Tudor and Stuart times, no parish seemed to be without a witch.

St Osyth and Manningtree had the dreadful misfortune of being home to local officials who were quick to take advantage of the legislation of the time. This was responsible for bringing countless old women to the gallows. They never questioned the bizarre evidence which came their way, but instead took a malicious pleasure in repeating every fragment of foul village gossip.

Another part of Essex where romance and the sinister mingle is Epping Forest. John Clare loved to hear the songs of the nightingale, red cap, sparrow and cuckoo, but for most eighteenth-century travellers the forest was a place of danger. Here were cutpurses and highwaymen swift to relieve the unwary of their belongings. The highwaymen Stephen Bunce and Sixteen-String Jack attracted admiration for going about their business with style and humour, but Dick Turpin and the Essex Gang were a criminal fraternity, deserving of total contempt for their viciousness.

As you move further south, you enter the towns that are on the fringe of London and have become swallowed up by an urban life where few folk stories survive, although Southend and Leigh-on-Sea have some interesting tales. Indeed, Essex is a county that seems almost to be five separate worlds – the coast, the marshes, the farming land, the pretty villages and the towns dominated by London. Part of the pleasure of writing this book has been discovering the lesser-known corners of Essex. I have been fascinated by the marshes around Tollesbury, the romantic villages that cluster around Saffron Walden, the coastal inlets around Paglesham and the pubs of Leigh-on-Sea. It's amazing how few people really explore these areas. They are well worth a leisurely visit.

I have to admit my own life in Essex has been centred around the Colchester area, but it has proved a fertile place for stories.

When I first began telling traditional oral stories with the Essex Storytellers, we worked on projects to do with the islands of Essex, the Battle of Maldon, the Mersea Barrow and the witches of Manningtree – and were amazed at the amount of unknown material we discovered.

The heritage of Essex is Saxon, for, as the name suggests, it is the land of the East Saxons. Its patron saint is St Cedd, who inspired the building of the evocative little stone chapel St Peter-on-the-Wall at Bradwell. There is also a fascinating wooden church from that time at Greenstead. The most exciting archaeological find in recent times has been the burial chamber of a Saxon king at Prittlewell in south-east Essex, whose importance has still not been fully appreciated.

Equally inspiring is that great epic poem *The Battle of Maldon*, which makes a hero of a man who lost a battle! Unfortunately, many of the folk stories that were told in the medieval period have been lost. The problem was that no one had systematically gathered these tales, except for local historians. Sadly their work is often hidden in local libraries in thin booklets, which tend to disappear down the back of dusty shelves. One of the most useful local histories is the attractively presented *Boxted: Portrait of an English Village* by Douglas Carter, because it shows the wealth of stories within one village. I feel that I have been on a quest to unearth hidden treasure and, amazingly, sometimes I have found it.

When I was first invited to put together a collection of Essex folk tales, I was a little concerned about the number of dark stories of witches, ghosts, murders and devils, but as I began researching the full range of tales I made all sorts of interesting discoveries. I found six dragons, an Anglo-Saxon king's burial chamber, and a lovely lady known as Edith Swan-neck. There were various White Ladies, a headless saint, a bad-tempered brownie and a magic scarecrow … read on to find out more, for it is Essex's diversity which makes it fascinating.

I found that breaking the stories into themes made it simpler to track down material and get a firmer understanding of what the tales were trying to convey. In telling these stories I have sometimes kept close to historical sources or told traditional tales, but in others I have used mere fragments of tales and history and woven them into a very personal yarn. Surely this is the storyteller's privilege? Much depends on the audience. The tale you tell in a pub is not the same as the epic you tell in a lecture theatre. Sometimes I want to make people laugh, sometimes I want to make the listener think about the human condition, and at other times I want to preserve precious relics of the past.

Always (as the old storytellers used to say) there is an apple for whoever listens to the story, there is an apple for whoever tells the story, and an apple for the storytellers of the past who have stood and whispered their tales in our ears. Peter, I owe you a lot of apples, for you are always my most faithful listener!

One

Here be Dragons

Roll up! Roll up! Today we present, for your special delight, six of Essex's finest dragons!

Essex's dragon stories concern real villages in Essex, which still take pride in these whimsical tales. Often the stories are unknown in the rest of the country. Saffron Walden has the most frightening dragon of all because it is a basilisk, which can kill simply with a glance from its eyes. Wormingford's dragon is a crocodile and East Horndon's is a snake newly arrived off a ship.

The dragon stories were once so popular that villages competed for their ownership. The Essex village of Wormingford and the Suffolk village of Bures both claimed the same dragon. Wormingford (once called Withermundford) actually went one step further, for the village's name was developed from the word 'worm', a medieval name for a dragon. Wormingford Church has a splendid stained-glass window with the 'coccodil' busily swallowing a plump pair of legs, watched by a knight in armour on a horse and a fleeing maiden.

Essex folk are eager to tell you that, according to a document at Canterbury Cathedral, an unusual fight broke out near Little Cornard on the afternoon of Friday 26 September 1449.

In a marshy field on the Suffolk/Essex Border, two fire breathing dragons engaged in a fierce hour long struggle. The Suffolk

Dragon was black and lived on Keddington Hill, while the dragon from Essex was reddish and spotted and came from Ballington Hill, south of the river Stour. Eventually the red dragon won and both creatures returned to their own hills to the admiration of many beholding them.

So Essex won!

The source for the Saffron Walden story and the Henham dragon is a pamphlet published in 1669 called 'The Flying Serpent' or 'Strange News out of Essex'. Strange news it certainly was! The stories were obviously concocted by William and Henry Winstanley. A jolly pair of jokers they seem to have been. William was a skilled conjurer, often fashioning dragon kites for his family. Henry built the first Eddystone Lighthouse and filled his House of Wonders at Littlebury with clockwork ghosts, robot servants, and trick chairs that suddenly whizzed people from the drawing room to the cellar or out into the garden. He even had Magic Dragons as a main attraction in his water theatre at Piccadilly. So it was simple for him to make a fake dragon.

Whatever their sources, these tales of Essex dragons make fine entertainment because of the undercurrent of humour. Yet you wonder. Could they contain an element of truth?

~ The Coccodil's Story ~

Once there was a king who was given an egg as a farewell present by the man he had fought for so long. How strange you say! Yet it is true. The great leader Saladin gave it to Richard the Lionheart when he left the Holy Land. The two may have been on opposite sides in the Crusade, but Saladin had a respect for the brave Englishman.

'This will keep you safe,' he said as he handed the English king the egg.

'Really?' Richard the Lionheart gazed down at the egg. It was a puzzle. There was nothing for it but to keep the egg as safe as he could in his saddlebags. Anything which kept him safe was to be treasured. His journey was going to take him through Germany, which he knew well enough was a place hostile to him. He had already disguised himself as a pilgrim to protect himself from possible robbers. It was not, however, to prove an effective disguise. Very quickly he found himself kidnapped by no less a person than Leopold, Duke of Austria.

In Richard's prison cell, the egg hatched into what at first looked like a tadpole and then a baby dragon. It kept the King amused while ransom arrangements were being made. The King made cooing noises at it until he realised it was growing alarmingly bigger and bigger. By the time he reached England, it was enormous! The King felt it safer to put the animal in the menagerie at the Tower of London. The menagerie keeper knew immediately what it was and he called it a 'coccodil' in that funny medieval way of his. It would be called a crocodile now.

'Majesty,' the keeper said, 'this coccodil is a fearsome creature. It will grow until it be twenty cubits long with a crested head, teeth like a saw and a tail extending to this length ...' He extended his arms to try to show the length, but his arms were inadequate.

'How shall we take care of it? It could eat us all up.'

'Build it a strong cage, and keep it well fed and locked up in chains.'

The keeper did what was asked of him, but, by the end of a year, it had grown so big that it lashed its tail against the bars with such force that the bars broke. With a mighty crashing it was free of its chains at last. Down into the Thames it slid joyfully and then up it went, splashing through rivers and sliding through muddy marshes. On and on it swam through Essex, always travelling at night. The only signs it left behind were the mangled corpses of young men and women foolish enough to be out after midnight.

Swimming, crawling and ravaging its way, it came to a village called Withermundford on the river Stour. Total panic broke out at the very sight of those long jaws opening and closing, revealing spiked teeth from which nothing could escape. The Lord of the Manor sent out his archers to kill the coccodil, but the arrows bounced off its back as if it had been made of iron or hard rock, and the arrows that fell onto the spine made a tinkling sound just as if they had fallen on a bronze plate. The animal's hide was totally impenetrable.

Then, worst of all, came the rumour that the coccodil was demanding the flesh of virgins for its food, for even in the best-regulated community there is only a limited supply of virgins! The entire community wrung their hands in distress at the very thought of losing their sweetest maidens.

'Send for Sir George!' they shouted.

The only George known to the worthy villagers was a local Lord of the Manor called Sir George from Layer de la Haye, son of Eustice, Earl of Boulouge. He was a brave fellow and came swiftly enough through the forest to the ford where the creature waited. The sight of the coccodil glaring at him made him nervous. Yet the people were shouting encouragement at him. He could not let them down, especially those lovely girls, with their hands over their mouths, suppressing their screams.

He advanced three paces at a time, then suddenly stopped. Carefully he lifted his lance high. The coccodil suddenly leapt up to reach for the knight's plump left leg. As soon as its jaw crunched the armoured thigh, the pain of biting into plate armour was too much for the coccodil and it disappeared into the water, swallowed up in the mere, leaving behind a trail of bubbles and the cheers of lots of relieved people.

Even to this day many have noticed how the water of the mere gets agitated at times. Bubbles rise again to the surface. There is a whistling wind in the reeds and the strange water plants wave desperately. The wise nod their heads. They know what it is. It can only be the descendant of the mighty coccodil, cautiously seeking a plump virgin. Watch and see where the bubbles go!

~ The Glass Knight ~

'What's happening?' The people of Saffron Walden just could not understand it. Fruit was rotting on the tree. Birds were dropping dead from the sky. The rivers were poisoned. They were terrified. Soon there would be nothing left to eat or drink.

'It's the fault of that thing ... that monster ... that dragon,' a local farmer moaned. 'I have seen it in the fields and it's terrible. It just opens its mouth and puffs out that foul breath and then everything living in its path dies ...' As he talked, fear got the better of him, and he could no longer speak properly.

In the end, the sheriff said, 'Let's go and see the wise woman. Maybe she can explain it.' A small crowd gathered and followed him. They too wanted to hear what she had to say.

The wise woman was waiting for them on top of the hill. Her head nodded and nodded on her skinny neck as she greeted them. 'Ah! You have come. I have been expecting this. I have seen the beast myself and know what damage it does.' Very gently she patted the farmer's arms and encouraged him to tell everybody what the dragon looked like.

'It has the head and claws of a rooster.' For a moment the farmer half expected the people to laugh at him but they did not. His terror was too obviously real. Encouraged by the fact that they were taking him seriously, the farmer babbled on. 'It has the forked tongue of a serpent which swings backwards and forwards. It has the wings of a bat and a long arrow-shaped tail like … like the Devil. All over its body there are barbs.'

'And what colour is it?'

'Every shade of black and yellow, with a white spot like a crown on its head. And it walks upright on two strong legs with a mighty tail …'

This seemed to match the diagrams that the wise woman had found in her well-thumbed *Book of the World's Most Hideous Creatures*. Then she drew breath and asked the question that was obviously the most important of all. 'What are his eyes like?'

The farmer shook his head. He did not know. He had not looked into the dragon's eyes.

The wise woman's nods grew more and more frequent. She was growing increasingly agitated. 'I knew it! I knew you could not have looked into his eyes. You would have been dead if you had. I must warn you all. This monster is a basilisk!' she screamed. She waved her skinny finger at the crowd in warning. 'Never look into its eyes, for its baleful glance will kill any living creature. The basilisk is the rarest and most dangerous of dragons.'

She began to give all sorts of magical descriptions, using proper technical terms. Not everybody present understood all this mumbo jumbo, but they could sense the danger they were in. The town's sheriff advised that a knight be sent for, a knight with experience of rescuing other towns in danger.

'Yes. Yes!' the people all said.

The sheriff galloped off to see what could be done. Sighing with relief, the people went home to the safety of their warm beds.

It took a while to find a suitable knight. Sadly, some foolish people could not wait. They had to see the dragon for themselves and ventured into the street, only to be confronted directly by the dreadful eyes of the basilisk. One glance and death was immediate. The number of bodies lying in the street was alarming. If the killings were allowed to continue, there could be a severe decline in the population. The basilisk was such an enthusiastic maneater. Nothing seemed to deter him.

The knight was terrified to be told of all the basilisk's powers. The good people of Saffron Walden, it was clear, were in peril. He went to his room at the inn immediately to begin his preparations. Gloomily he polished his armour late into the night, going over and over the difficulties of fighting this sort of dragon. He was rapidly coming to the conclusion that he had taken on more than he could cope with. How could he kill such a ferocious maneater? How could he avoid the breath that burns all in front of it? It could not be defeated by a sword or a spear, for its poisonous blood would flow the length of the weapon like lighting, withering the body of the person holding it. There are some, however, who say that in this situation the herb rue can have healing qualities.

And those eyes! How hideous they were! It was curious that the beast only closed his eyes when he drank water from a pool. Did that hold a clue to its weakness? He was determined to find some way to help these people.

Right up until dawn, the knight tossed and turned; and you know how it is – sometimes in our sleep we get the answer to our most nagging problems. He woke to an early sun, feeling far more cheerful, yet he did not rush into action yet. He had something to arrange first. The people watched from behind their shuttered windows, getting more and more restless, but they had faith in the knight. Then one of the village lads caught a glimpse of the knight riding to the field where the basilisk lay.

'He's here. Hurrah!'

'Whatever is he wearing?'

'Whatever it is, I can see myself reflected in it.'

'It's a suit of armour made of crystal mirrors!'

'Whatever good will that do? He's got no sword. He's carrying rue and a sprig of magic rowan.'

Silence fell. The people had lost their faith in the knight, but slowly they followed him through the trees that lined the road. Then they stopped when he stopped. The knight stood in front of the basilisk with his eyes tightly closed. The monster itself rose up on its legs and stared at the knight, its baleful eyes glittering with malice and then, with an almighty shriek of pain, the loathsome creature saw itself reflected in the armour's crystal glass. The horror of the moment seemed to freeze him into complete immobility. The beast fell and was still; still in the finality of its death, caused by looking into its own toxic eyes.

No one moved. Then the knight rolled the basilisk's corpse into a hole in the ground and scattered it with rue to eliminate any trace of poison. An almighty cheer echoed on all sides.

Drums, tabors and fiddles began playing and the people danced. All day and all night they danced, some dancing as far as Thaxted, and some say the dancing still goes on when the people remember their lucky escape.

And if you still doubt this tale, then know that the knight's sword was hung in Saffron Walden Church, and an effigy of the basilisk was set up in brass, with a table close by which told the entire story. Then, in the time of the Great Rebellion (or Civil War as some will call it), this was all taken down as being some monument to superstition. Lawless soldiers broke it into pieces.

Well, I say those fellows were no better than the basilisk for trying to destroy a fine thing! We should rebuild a monument to the crystal knight in today's troubled times. Courage and inventiveness should always be celebrated.

⚊ STRANGE NEWS OUT OF ESSEX ⚊

Edgar never forgot the summer of 1669; the summer he was nine years old and the dragon came to Henham. Such a noise and chatter! Nobody could quite believe it. It was the strangest news ever heard in Essex. To think a flying serpent had come to Henham, lovely little Henham on the hill! Some called it a dragon. Yet I want you to listen carefully; there's something about this tale that doesn't quite hang together.

Edgar was most impressed with the story told by a fine gentleman wearing a splendid blue velvet suit and riding a grey mare. It may have been because the fine gentleman, riding out on that May morning, had caught the first glimpse of the Henham dragon. He announced to the villagers on his return, 'I tell you, I have never been so frightened in my life. I was riding past the farm they call the Lodge, minding my own business, when without any warning the dragon came out of the meadow. It attacked me and my horse. It was quite, quite terrifying to see a creature of such monstrous size rise up in that way before us. I swear to you, I was convinced the horse and I were close to death. I gripped the mare firmly with my thighs, and spurred her homewards. As I galloped, I caught a glimpse of the farmer who owned the field where the beast sat. I shouted to him, 'Quick! Quick! Get your cattle indoors. They're in danger! The dragon will have them.' I can tell you the farmer's face was as pale as cheese. He did not hesitate. He crossed to his fields with his dog at his heels and his droving stick in his hand, and immediately directed his cattle up to his cowshed. I never stopped to see if he got there safely. I just wanted to get home and warn you all what I had seen.'

A few days later another story came from two men in the same parish. Mind you, they came out of the pub so Edgar was not sure what to make of their tale, although it had a lot more detail to it. They said that they had seen the dragon on a hillock sunning himself. He was stretched out to his fullest extent, so it was easy to get a true impression of the size of the creature. It was gigantic!

'We were armed with clubs and staves, yet we dared not get any closer. The dragon lolled over onto his chest and seemed to be challenging us to approach him. Now the way I would describe him was he was eight or nine foot long, the smallest part of him being the size of a man's leg, and the middle of him as big as a man's thigh. His eyes were very large and piercing. In his mouth he had two rows of teeth which appeared very white and sharp, and on his back he had two rather small wings. The wings did not seem in proportion to the rest of his body. We thought those wings would seem too weak to carry such an unwieldy body.'

The crowd that had gathered to hear this story were getting more and more interested. 'What did you do?'

'We were not sure how we should proceed. I went off to get a gun and my brother watched the dragon, which still stood as though it was totally unafraid. Then it seemed to lose patience and went off to the woods making as much noise as a wild boar rustling its way through the leaves.'

It seemed incredible that so many grown-ups seemed to believe these stories. For the rest of that summer, group after group of men set out to find this scary beast. They were well-armed with guns, muskets and fowling pieces. Yet the creature did not emerge again, although surely it must have been hungry. The other thing that was puzzling was that all the people who went to see the dragon returned looking remarkably cheerful. What was going on? People like a churchwarden, a constable and an overseer of the poor had given evidence of sighting the dragon, so there had to be some truth in it.

Then, one day, young Edgar bumped into his cousin, Noah. Noah was older than he was and thought he knew everything. Noah guessed exactly what Edgar had on his mind. 'I know what you're going to ask. You're going to ask about that dratted dragon again. Come with me and I'll show you something.'

The boy found himself being taken to one of the outhouses at Mr Henry Winstanley's house. It was growing dusk but it was still possible to see that lying on the straw was the outline of something that looked like some misshapen monster.

'Go on. Get closer. Take a proper look at it.' Noah pushed Edgar closer. For a moment he trembled. Then he touched it. It seemed to be made of canvas and wood. 'Go on, put it on. Oh you big baby. Let me show you.' Noah slipped the contraption over his head and sure enough he looked just like the dragon in the field.

'Who ever made a thing like this?'

'Henry Winstanley of course! Don't you remember those dragon kites Henry made? Well, he did this and his uncle spread the story in his magazine.'

'But so many people joined in with the silliness and they were all adults!'

'Oh don't look so solemn. It was a prank. Adults like a good story just like us and you have to admit it's a jolly yarn. Don't spoil it. Keep it to yourself. It could make the village famous.'

Sure enough, for a while it did. Henham village had an annual fair to sell models of the monster. Even today, on the village website, a dragon flutters across the page. I can promise you, the dragon would have a warm welcome if he were to be seen again in Henham. They like a good joke there.

~ THE FLAMING DRAGON ~

On 9 March 1104 Ralph Niger reported that a dragon had attacked the Abbey of Chich at the village St Osyth. It was a dragon of 'marvellous bigness'. The air around it was so hot that the area was set alight. Sadly nothing more was heard about it. Today, the crumbling image of a dragon can still be seen carved into the spandrels of the abbey gateway.

~ THE DRAWSWORDS SERPENT ~

In a field with the picturesque name of Drawswords, in the village of Great Bentley, there was once a lady dragon sufficiently fierce to prevent anybody from attempting to remove her from her special place. The villagers discussed many ideas and were rather delighted to discover she had a taste for beer. Carefully they left out a vat of beer and, as you can imagine, she fell asleep for days at a time. But the supply of ale began to run out.

Inevitably, the people had to summon a dashing young hero to fight the beast, and indeed he did an excellent job, actually impaling the dragon on his sword and bearing her in triumph to the village green where it would be possible for many people to view her, for Great Bentley has one of the largest village greens in England. Sadly for him, as he held her so proudly aloft a spot of venom from her massive jaws fell on his foot. And that was the end of him.

And what of the dragon? She vanished, but there are still odd sightings of her ghost and the odd hiss which suggests she is about looking for her beer. So if you live in Great Bentley, leave a little on the doorstep for her.

~ THE BARBARY SERPENT ~

It had been a long voyage and the night was cold and wet and dark as the ship drew into the Thames estuary. The Barbary merchants, who owned the splendid vessel, decided to drop anchor and rest. It was best, they thought, to wait for daylight to find a port to unload their cargo, for they could see nothing clearly through the driving rain.

The crew slept so well that none of them saw the vast writhing creature that uncurled itself in the hold, nor did they see this fearsome serpent slither up on deck and over the sides of the prow. There was a splosh as it fell in the water, but not loud enough to wake anybody. Confused and angry at finding itself in such dank water, the serpent kept on swimming until it found a beach that was safe enough for it to curl up on and sleep.

The next day it moved inland until it reached the woods surrounding the isolated village of East Horndon, some miles from Brentwood. Amazingly, it managed to survive despite the cold, and maybe because it so terrorised the area that nobody came near it. The serpent grew more and more hungry and slid its way to the churchyard, where it huddled up against a gravestone for warmth.

One day at dusk, a girl who was hunting for berries and nuts fell against the gravestone. She looked in total horror as the creature untwisted itself from its hiding place. On and on it went writhing skywards, until it reached high above the child's head. The girl could not take her eyes off the serpent's purple tongue, which twisted menacingly above her.

'Oh God in heaven! It's a great worm! It's a dragon!' the girl shouted. Ducking and diving, she managed to back away from the creature.

The village was tiny, so it did not take long for everybody to hear about this terror that had come to their village. The villagers talked about it and decided there was only one conclusion. They must go to see Sir James Tyrell, the Lord of the Manor. After all, it must be the responsibility of the Lord of the Manor to get rid of such creatures. A deputation of village worthies set off for Heron Hall to request that the monster be removed immediately.

Sir James was not pleased. This was not the sort of adventure he craved, but the honour of his family was at stake. They had never quite lived down the scandal of the ancestor who had accidentally shot William Rufus in the New Forest. The ancestor had only got himself out of trouble by saying that he had caught a glimpse of the King's red hair and had mistaken him for a red squirrel! Since then, the Tyrells had been regarded as totally untrustworthy by the royal family and had not been allowed to go within the walls of London.

A sudden outburst of family pride overtook him and Sir James at last donned his black armour and blue-plumed helmet. The blacksmith had given a really sharp edge to his sword and lance. Sir James hung a mirror to his breastplate. He must show himself the true hero.

'What's the mirror for?' Alice, his wife, demanded.

'Do you know nothing, silly woman? Dragons are vain and the light blazing from my chest will totally confuse him.' Listening to no more of his wife's misgivings, he set off for the graveyard.

The dragon had not moved from its hiding place. Hearing the knight approaching, he slunk out onto the grass. As the knight had foretold, the serpent reached up to see his refection in the glass on the knight's chest. Swiftly, the knight drew his sword and a mighty fight was underway. It was obvious that

Sir James was stronger, but it still took an almighty effort to finish the dragon off as he sawed his way through its neck, skilfully beheading the creature. Proudly he bore the serpent's head home to show his wife.

Sadly, as she took him in her arms to kiss him, the terrible exertion of the fight overcame Sir James and he fell to the ground and died. Poor Lady Alice! Her troubles were not over. Their son raced down to see the carcass of the dead beast, only to fall over it and break his leg. His wounds festered and sadly he too passed away.

All that could be done was to record the great deed in a stained-glass window at Heron Hall and to tell the story to succeeding generations, just as I am telling it to you now.

Two

Battles Long Ago

It is strange that although Romans, Saxons, Vikings and Normans fought their battles many centuries ago, the way their stories are told now depends very much on the attitude of the modern storyteller. Take the story of Boudicca. She has been a favourite to feminists, imperialists and even admirers of Mrs Thatcher. I have chosen to tell her story in a very Celtic way and to set her last battle, according to an Essex tradition, in Ambresbury Banks. No one really knows where her last battle was fought, or how she died or where she was buried. Only fragments of folklore live on. A rather interesting suggestion was that her last battle was fought on the site of King's Cross station and she was buried under Platform Nine!

There are so many mysteries from the days of those early battles. Why did Byrhtnoth, the Anglo-Saxon leader, allow the attacking Vikings to cross the causeway to the mainland, so that the Saxons lost the distinct advantage of penning the Vikings in on Northey Island? To find the answer you have to read that magnificent Anglo-Saxon epic *The Battle of Maldon*. Its rhythms and visual images have seeped into my telling.

The ghosts of those fallen heroes still haunt us. Skilled journalist James Wentworth Day's meetings with the lively characters he met while wild fowling gave him some amazing material. Charles Stamp, one of his most regular companions, told him about the Viking at the Battle of Benfleet. You cannot help but sympathise with the chieftain who lost his ships.

But the Vikings were actually figures of terror for many centuries. I strongly think that the popularity of devils in medieval Essex stories was a memory of the horrors of Danish attacks. Several churches claim to have Viking skin pinned to their doors; a punishment for the Vikings' plundering ways.

There is also the mystery of what really happened to Harold Godwinson after the Battle of Hastings. Did he actually live on after the battle? I must admit I prefer the more romantic story of Edith Swan-neck taking his body back to Waltham Abbey. I have my own opinion as to what were the 'lover's marks' on his body, which actually could be historically correct according to William of Malmesbury's description of the English fashions of the time.

And finally, a touch of humour, suitable for a Welsh woman, has been added to the medieval story of the King's standard bearer.

~ BOUDICCA'S LAST STAND ~

The battle was about to begin. The old Druid bunched his robes around him and struggled onto one of the baggage wagons behind the Iceni warriors. They were among the hills of the fortress that the ancient folk had built. The site was known as

Ambresbury Banks. Above him the Druid saw birds, and knew
in his heart by the way the birds flew that all was not well. He
had the skill of divining. The women in the wagon next to
him, however, were in high spirits. They could not even think
of defeat. Had they not gone from one victory to another?
Colchester, London and Verulamium had all fallen so easily.
Their eyes were on their queen, standing in her chariot with her
two daughters on either side.

Boudicca was looking at her most magnificent. Her great mass
of tawny hair rippled down to her hips. Her eyes were blazing.
Around her neck shone the golden torc of a Celtic leader. Behind
her a wind blew out her wildly coloured tunic. A fine brooch held
her cloak in position. Then suddenly, as she lifted her spear high,
silence fell among her warriors.

The Queen's voice was harsh, but that day it rang out clearly. 'I
know that it is not the first time Britons have been led by a woman,
but I have not come to boast about my family. You know why I
am here. I come to recover my kingdom and its plundered wealth.
I have come to restore the rights of my people. I have come to
revenge the torture of the Roman lash on my back. I come for
vengeance for the rape of my daughters. The Romans know what
they have done. Look at their army now. See how they cower before
us! See how many of us there are compared to them. The dead of
Colchester and London will be as nothing compared to what we
do here. We will not falter. We will fight to the end. Victory will
be ours.'

Cheers broke out all around her and fists were raised to the
heavens. For a moment Boudicca caught the eye of the aged
Druid. She saw he was looking across at the Roman leader,
Suetonius Paulinus. The Roman leader had a look of contempt
on his face. It was also clear how cleverly his troops were
arranged – the infantry legions were placed in the centre with

their auxiliaries beside them, and beyond them the cavalry on either wing. Queen and Druid looked anxious but the Iceni did not hesitate. They were on the move.

Then suddenly it all went wrong. A hideous hail of Roman javelins blackened the sky, followed by the thrust of well-disciplined shields and those deadly short swords. The Iceni had no room to wield their longer swords or any way of using their chariots. Such turmoil! So terrible a confusion! The war chariots became entangled with the baggage wagons. Old women and children were stampeded to their deaths. Even the oxen pulling the wagons were slaughtered.

The old man was quick-witted. He had jumped down from the wagon and made his way to the surrounding trees. It was clear to him that any attempt at escape by the Iceni was being stopped by the pincer movement of the Roman cavalry. It was a rout for Boudicca's army, a humiliating defeat.

The Druid hoped the Queen would find her way into the middle of the forest to the circle of trees that he called his 'sacred grove'. It was said to be a place where no birds perched on the branches nor wild beasts made their lairs; where the trees were safe from thunder and lightning yet quivered in the slightest wind. Few ever came to that place, but the Druid knew the Queen and her daughters would surely come. In fact, they had arrived by the time the thin golden light of dawn broke.

He was ready for them. He had the bowls prepared. The bright red berries of the yew were laid out against their green leaves. The women knew that what they were about to drink was poison. They were not alarmed. As they lost consciousness and sank into the undergrowth, they seemed almost to sigh with relief. No doubt they were prepared for the Other Life and, even more importantly, they would be saved from the forced humiliating march through Rome.

The bodies were not found the next day, or the next day, or the day after that. In fact they have never been found, but the three women still drive their chariot on through our dreams.

~ THE BATTLE OF MALDON ~

It is a hot day in August, AD 991. By the banks of the Blackwater, voices echo across the channel between Northey Island and the mainland. Every sound is clear. From the safety of Northey Island, the Viking herald shouts this challenge to Byrhtnoth's Saxon army: 'Tribute! We want tribute. Give us tribute. Gold or silver will suit. Then we'll leave you in peace.'

From the opposite shore of the causeway, where Byrhtnoth's people wait for battle, comes the gentle drone of women praying. 'Deliver us, O Lord, from the fury of the Norseman.' Their heads are full of stories of the horrors of the Vikings' attack on Ipswich. They wish a tribute would be paid. It could save so many lives.

Their men think differently. Their leader is determined. 'Listen, you sea wolves, all we are sending you are our spears and our arrows. That will be our tribute. Here I stand, Byrhtnoth, the ealdorman of Essex, and it is my duty to guard this place for our King Aethelred and his people. No one shall invade it.'

Byrhtnoth's shield and ash spear are raised high and his men beat their shields. Behind him, their war cry is shouted. The sound is growing louder and louder across the water 'Byrhtnoth! Byrhtnoth! Byrhtnoth!'

The battle begins. The causeway is covered in water. Ah, the tide is turning! The Saxons are advancing, inflicting a terrible revenge. The Vikings are desperate. They are pleading for the battle to continue on the dry, level ground of the mainland.

Byrhtnoth has agreed! Why is he doing this? Is it a foolish decision or a misguided sense of fairness? Somehow it does not seem to matter. Byrhtnoth's men will do anything for him.

Here is a man of magnificent courage. Here is a man who looks every inch a hero. He stands 6ft 9in tall with swan-white hair and the stance of a noble beast.

A Viking spear comes hurtling towards the chief, which he parries with his shield. His blood is roused. Just look at that face. He may be old, but he aims his dart into his attacker's throat with deadly accuracy and the man falls dead. He laughs. 'I'll conquer yet, I'll lay you low.' As if to show his strength, his next victim is pierced in the chest, even through his chain mail.

'Watch out!' From behind him comes a spear that pierces his body. Somehow one of his young soldiers manages to remove that spear and hurls it back, so his master's attacker falls in the dirt.

Around the fallen leader, hovering like the ravens over the battlefield, are Vikings waiting to loot from him as he lies on the ground. They want his clothes, his rings and his richly worked sword. Yet somehow he has enough strength to raise his sword. Again comes a terrible blow. A Viking axe shatters his shoulder. Byrhtnoth is exhorting his men to keep on fighting. He is looking to heaven. He knows how it shall be.

'Let me come to you, King of Angels, take my soul to heaven and let no demon come near.' So this is it! His last moment!

And there are demons in this place for the sea wolves are hacking at his body. Even within his own camp there are traitors. Look at Godric. He has leapt on the very steed his lord had ridden and he is riding for the safety of the woods with his two brothers.

Yet the loyalty of Byrhtnoth's army remains unshaken. They fight on, determined to avenge their fallen leader. Shield rims snap and chain mail seems to sing out a gruesome hymn. The light is fading. The mud and the maiming have so mangled the dead bodies that only a strip of embroidery or a cloak clasp proves who lies beneath the swirling seagulls. A young woman is cradling the body of the fallen leader, wrapped in her cloak, so the widow cannot see that the head has been hacked off by the enemy.

It's been a victory of sorts for the Vikings, although they have scarcely enough men left to man their ships. The only treasure with which they leave is the head of Byrhtnoth.

Yet the men of Essex have a greater task, for the body of Byrhtnoth, ealdorman of Essex, is to be taken to be buried in the magnificent abbey in Ely. Somewhere in the camp a poet lifts his harp, but he is slow to sing. The grief is too new. Eventually the poet finds his voice. The names that he sings are the dead who fell on the battlefield. The names are taken on the wind and, as time passes, this epic tale of the men of Essex's unfailing courage shall pass from mouth to mouth from one millennium to another.

Curlews call and the tale is retold.

~ THE VIKING WHO LOST HIS SHIPS ~

This is the tale, as it was told to Wentworth Day, of a Viking ghost who appeared to Charlie Stamp. It happened in Charles' wooden shanty cottage, facing the mouth of the Thames under the sea wall of Canvey Island.

I laid in me truckle bed upstairs one night last week and I looked over the top of the wall to the tide a'flowing in. Bright moonlight that was. Bright as day. All of a sudden I seed a man come wading ashore. He was knee deep when I fust clapped eyes on him, kickin' up the spray. Then he got into the mud and come straight to this cottage. He knew how to walk on mud too, long striding strides, same as you and I when you don't dig your toes and heel in. Otherwise you'd get stuck. Well he sort of skated across the mud, same as us, got into the saltings, jumped a rill or two and then came over the top of the sea wall. He crossed the plank over the dyke, and next thing I knowed he was in my room. Tall handsome chap he was with long golden hair flowing down like a gal's. He wore a sort of tunic with a leather jerkin over it and cross gartering below his knees. He had a long droopy moustache, a rare old snout on him like an eagle, blue eyes and a helm on his head. That must have been steel 'cos it flashed in the moonlight. And there was a pair of wings sticking out of it, one on each side. He looked down at me right sorrowful and he say 'Mate, I lost me ship. I want to git home, beyond the seas. Can you help me?'

'Go you down to Grays or Tilbury, owd mate' I says. 'There's forever o' the ships come in there. You find one to take you to any port in the world.' He looks at me again, shook his head and said sorrowfully like, 'You don't understand. I've lost me ship. I've lost me country. I'm a lost man.'

And with that, sir, he went out of the winder, all six foot of him and over the sea wall, across the saltings and down onto the mud and into the tide. He waded under the moon, his helm aflashing in the moonlight and then he vanished. The sea swallered him up. Who do you reckon that was, sir?

Without a doubt we would all answer 'a Viking', except that possibly, being better informed, we would add that the Viking helmets did not have wings attached.

Who was this lost man who had lost his ships and lost his country? Well, there are clues. The *Anglo-Saxon Chronicle* speaks of a battle at Benfleet fought between the Saxons and the Vikings. The Vikings had moved into Benfleet in the years before the battle to work as shipwrights. Benfleet was perfect, for it had water and timber in abundance, and it was hidden from the main stream so was well suited as a fortified camp. Its Danish name, *Beamfleote*, meant wood and water.

In AD 894, the Viking commander, Haesten the Black, had taken his men plundering in the surrounding area in order to get supplies. Because of the tragedy that overcame him, this is the most likely person to have later appeared to Charlie Stamp. You see, Haesten left behind eighty ships and, he thought, enough men to guard his wife and sons and the other women and children. He was wrong. Hidden by thick forest and marshland, a Saxon army led by Alfred the Great's son Edward and his son-in-law Ethelred came up from London. What a terrible surprise the attack on the Viking fort was! Viking ships were either burnt down to the waterline or taken to London. Men were killed. Some Vikings ran away to Shoeburyness.

When Haesten returned, he found to his horror that his wife and children had been taken prisoner. Fortunately, Alfred felt an obligation to them. After an earlier skirmish, Alfred had made himself Haesten's sons' godfather. So when Haesten returned, Alfred, being a good Christian man, returned the Viking's family. Mind you, the fighting continued for a while. Haesten, despite the fact he was still known as 'a lusty and terrifying old warrior' seems to have vanished. Maybe he wandered around looking for his ships. No doubt he hesitated about attacking Alfred again after his children were returned to him. He may have returned to the sea, or maybe not.

What we do know is that, had his ghost hovered around until 1855, he may have caught a glimpse of his vessels again for, in that year, navvies working on a local railway line found the burnt-out timber of ships.

~ THE DANE'S SKIN ~

There is a rather macabre story told about many Essex churches. It is the story of a fragment of human skin found nailed to the church door. The usual explanation is that it is the skin of a Viking raider who was being punished for stealing church plate. The story was certainly told about Hadstock Church, near Saffron Walden.

In 2001 the BBC made a television series called *The Blood of the Vikings*; a fragment of the skin was taken from the Hadstock door and sent for DNA analysis at Oxford University. Disappointingly for the ghoulish, it turned out to be cow skin and not human after all, so the door had been covered in leather. No one is sure whether this was for decoration or as a draught excluder, but it did have the effect of stopping the natural acids in the oak door from corroding the iron door fittings.

The door itself is now being researched by the Society of Antiquaries; it was made between 1044 and 1067 from oak, which must have been at least 400 years old when it was felled. It is in fact the oldest church door still in use in the country. The arch around the door is a rebuild using Saxon stones with the honeysuckle moulding, also found in the crossing arches within the church itself.

~ EDITH SWAN-NECK ~

1066 – it's a year we all know, the year the Normans defeated the English, but few of us know the exact day. At dusk, on 14 October, the Battle of Hastings was finally won by the Normans.

It was a sad twist of fate. Up until that moment, the English had been hanging on manfully. Just one random arrow ended it all. Harold Godwinson, King of the English, fell to his death among a vast number of dismembered bodies. Many of these soldiers had been the King's own housecarls, who had struggled to the last to defend him.

In the confusion, only two monks from Waltham Abbey, Brothers Osegood and Ailric, searched desperately among the heaps of corpses to find the body of King Harold to take home for burial – but they were too late. Darkness fell too quickly. No moon appeared. Night seemed impenetrable. The hope of finding the King blacked out entirely and nothing but despair filled the hearts of the defeated.

In the morning, the monks began their search again, but it was an even more desperate task in daylight. Many of the faces of the English dead were gruesomely mutilated. It seemed the Normans had no shame. Not only would they disfigure faces, but they would steal the very clothes off the corpses' backs. Everywhere Norman soldiers could be seen slipping tunics of chain mail off dead bodies like a kitchen maid skinning a rabbit. No dignity was left for the dead.

The two monks in their black habits huddled together like displaced carrion crows. The question still hovered between them. How could they find their dead king in this place of bloody slaughter? It was young Osegood who eventually suggested, 'Only she who loves him best will recognise the dead body. We should send for her.'

He did not need to say more. The news had spread quickly. Even in the cloister, it was known that 'she who loves him best' was not Harold's wife but his mistress, Edith. It was accepted in royal circles that a simple 'hand-held relationship' was as binding as a formal marriage. Harold and Edith's six children surely showed their commitment to each other!

They found her searching, as they were, for their lost lord. 'I will find him,' she declared without embarrassment, 'for I know of the lover's marks on his body.' The monks blushed a little with embarrassment at her frankness. A sad little procession set out across the battlefield to the place where the English housecarls had set up a flag for their king. As she passed by, even the worst of brutes looked up to stare at her with respect. It was clear why she was called Edith the Fair. She was tall and slender. Her skin had a white, luminous glow. She walked with great grace, without pausing to lift her skirts from the mud and blood of the battlefield. Even the Normans scurried to try to make her path as easy as possible.

By the time she reached the English flag post, there appeared to have been an effort made to lay the bodies out in some sort of order, not in a hideous pile – although the faces were just as disfigured and bloody as they had been at the moment when they were killed. Most of the bodies were naked. She did not turn away. Several times she stopped to look more intently and several times her hand went to her face to wipe away her tears, but she said nothing.

Then she came to a man lying on his back with his arms outstretched above his head and the hair brushed into the blood of his injured face. She did not try to sweep back the hair. It was obvious the face would be unrecognisable from the battering it had received. She fell to her knees and felt the knotted muscles in his shoulder blades. She kissed his shoulders and then, separating his chest hair, she found a livid scar from a previous battle. She kissed that scar. She knew it well. Gently she turned over his arm. She even kissed away the dirt and blood, and a design could be seen emerging on the white flesh of the inner part of the elbow. It was tiny but clear enough. It was a blue tattoo of a swan lifting its long neck to reach for the sun. Most warriors had tattoos to show their military sympathies but her Harold had wanted his tattoo to celebrate her beauty, to celebrate the many kisses he had planted on her sweet neck.

She could bear it no longer. Suddenly she leant forward and pulled his body into her arms and rocked him backwards and forwards, singing some ancient lullaby. The grief was welling inside her and she wept copiously. All around her, silence fell.

No one knew what to do or say. They all felt awed by this outburst of sorrow. It was the old monk Ailric who at last eased Edith's precious burden from her arms and lifted her to her feet. 'Come my dear, we have found him now. We can take him home to Waltham Abbey. We can see his beloved cross again. It's the place we healed him isn't it, Edith Swan-neck?'

Something in his manner soothed her. The old monk was one of the few to know her old nickname. Only Harold called her Swan-neck to her face. She had remembered so many happy visits with Harold to Waltham Abbey, to the church he had helped consecrate. It had meant so much to them because the black flint cross on the altar had cured many an ailment. If they had only heeded it, she and Harold would have realised that misfortune was about to come to them for, when Harold had stopped to pray there before the battle, the figure on the cross had seemed to look away. Surely it was a sign that all was not well. Yet somehow she felt there would be a healing process when she returned with the body to the abbey. At last, Duke William gave his permission for them to leave with the body. Harold Godwinson, the last Anglo-Saxon king of England, would be buried at Waltham Abbey. It was fitting. Here, Edith of the lovely swan-neck might come to terms with her grief.

~ THE KING'S STANDARD BEARER ~

It was the best thing that had ever happened to Henry de Essex. The old honour awarded to his family, the swains of the manor of Thundersley, had been revived. He was to be the standard bearer to the King, no less a king than Henry II – and there was a king to be admired. When he walked into a room, there was a glow around that closely cropped red head and the grey eyes that missed nothing. He walked with the swagger of one used to commanding men.

It was 1157 when the two Henrys rode out for the first time to battle. It was to be in Wales, at a place called Coleshill in Flintshire. Wales! That land of rain-soaked barbarians! Nothing good could come of that. Yet the Welsh seemed to be on the retreat amazingly quickly. The English charged after them in full pursuit of the Welsh princes, but it was a trick. They had been led through the thick woods, down a narrow path into an ambush. Caught between the gnarled trees, the sections of the English army were separated. The standard bearer found his heavy horse sliding among the wet rocks. The clouds grew darker. The rain fell heavily. Every sound of falling rock reverberated around the mountains. The Welsh battle cry of 'Bara caws!' echoed so loudly that it made it seem as though their army was enormous.

Henry de Essex had become separated from many of his men. Only his faithful squire was able to reach his ear and whisper, 'The King is dead.' Henry felt the anguish of losing his king so strongly that he did not even feel the pain in his right hand from a flying arrow. He only realised what had happened when he saw the blood pouring onto the royal standard. The pain became uncontrollable. The stained banner fell from his hand. There seemed to be no point in hanging on if the King was dead.

He hung his head in grief and barely noticed his knights riding protectively behind him as they left the battle and rode for days, barely stopping to eat and drink, until at last they were forced to stop at an inn for refreshment. It was there they met an English survivor of the battle, who told Henry that the King had survived and had turned the battle into his victory. Henry de Essex was ashamed. He, the royal standard bearer, had left the field! How could he have doubted the King?

When he returned to court the King forgave him, but Henry could still hear the whispers – 'Coward!', 'Deserter!', 'Traitor!'. The whispering was like the hissing of steam in his brain. It would not go away and he was glad when six years later Robert de Montfort challenged him to mortal combat. Henry almost felt relieved. According to the beliefs of the time, in mortal combat God protected the innocent. Henry would be proved right.

The combat was held at Reading. The money was on Robert de Montfort for he was the stronger swordsman, but Henry fought like a man possessed. De Montfort slipped. The crowd went silent but it was a trick. He was on his feet and forcing Henry de Essex to drop his sword. Then he turned to the King and asked, 'Shall I kill him now?'

The King looked thoughtful and for a moment seemed to hesitate. Then he announced to the watchful crowd, 'I pardon your life, Henry de Essex, for the sake of past services, but the Lord has shown his will. Your land and possessions are forfeited to the Crown. You shall forsake all worldly things and become a monk here at the abbey at Reading.'

Henry de Essex left the royal presence with his head bowed. He knew he should be grateful to have his life saved but the bile of disgrace was in his mouth. He realised how much he was going to miss Thundersley and Rayleigh and his manor house at Jarvis Hall.

Time passed and time passed and Henry settled into the gentle rhythm of monastic routine. Gerald of Wales, the distinguished scholar, came to visit him one day. He was amusing company and had travelled so widely. Brother Henry offered him food.

'Just a little bara and caws,' the Welshman smiled.

Henry froze to hear those words again.

Gerald caught his bemused expression and translated the Welsh. 'Just bread, bread and cheese is all I want.'

'Bread and cheese? Is that all they wanted at the battle?'

'Battles have been fought for less.' Something in Gerald's tone seemed to suggest that battles were unimportant. The younger Henry de Essex would have protested, but the older Henry looked out at the cloister garden and smelt the lavender and the bay tree and felt only tranquillity. It was all such a long time ago. Such heartache over a piece of stained cloth!

Three

HERO OR VILLAIN?

One of the strangest features of English folk stories is that 'heroes' walk very close to the line of what is legal and what is not. Nowhere is that truer than in Essex, where local heroes are most often pirates, smugglers or highwaymen.

The story of the Fingringhoe pirate is told humorously and may originally have been inspired by a pirate seen hanging from a gibbet, with new growth spurting out of the wood. Today there is certainly a very splendid ancient oak growing by the village pond.

The geography of Essex lends itself to smuggling. In a book of 1904, called *Marsh-Country Rambles*, Herbert Tompkins wrote:

> Examine a large map of Essex and you will see how truly the county was made for smugglers. Run your eye along the marvellously contorted coastline from Shoeburyness to St Osyth point. There are at least 50 well defined rivers, creeks or outfalls; to search the coast for some notorious gang on a dark night was like looking for the proverbial needle in a haystack.

Smugglers were often supported by their local communities and even today you find villages where they are regarded with a kind of laughing approval; but then, 'Essex man' has always been a little against the Establishment. The same rebellious spirit affected their attitude to highwaymen, and the stories of Stephen Bunce and Sixteen-String Jack are told with obvious relish. Dick Turpin is a more difficult problem. I have given Black Bess a good press for it was her exploits that really made a bestseller out of William Harrison Ainsworth's novel *Rookwood*. *Rookwood* in turn made a hero out of Turpin, as did many ballads of the time. Eighteenth-century folk crowded to a highwayman's hanging and waited with excitement for ballads of his exploits. Yet it is in the ghost story 'The Widow's Rant' that I have shown Turpin's personality as it was known to those who had grown to fear the Essex Gang.

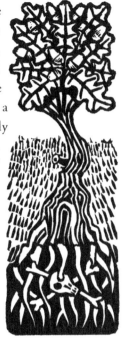

~ The Pirate's Heart ~

Peg Leg Jake, the black-hearted pirate of Doneyland, was coming home. Well, not straight to his mum's little cottage in Rowhedge. First he had to go on up the hill to Fingringhoe, you see, to visit his sweetheart. Everybody knew his Rosie's cheerful smile, not to mention her pert little bosom. It was Rosie who drew so many men to the Whale-Bone Inn.

Thump! Thump! Up the hill he went with his brand new wooden leg. He was feeling mighty proud of himself – plenty of pieces of eight in his pocket and no dratted parrot weighing down his right shoulder. The foolish bird had fallen off his perch only yesterday. Jake's nice new velvet jacket was free of bird droppings. And what tales of swashbuckling he had to tell! Ought to be worth a kiss or two. He flung open the door of the inn and banged on the table. 'Yo ho, ho and a bottle of rum.'

The door opened and his Rosie appeared. He pursed his lips ready for a kiss, but nothing! Not even a girlish giggle.

'Go away, I'm busy.' She disappeared into the garden with a full tray of foaming tankards and that little swaying of the hips that always made him smile. He watched her go with his mouth open. This was not the welcome he had been expecting. He heard the singing:

> Hearts of oak are our ships,
> Jolly tars are our men.
> We always are ready,
> Steady, boys, steady,
> To victory we call you again and again.

Then he saw who they were. They were a jolly bunch of young tars from His Majesty's Navy. It was obvious that they too were impressed by Rosie's charms. She was experienced enough a serving wench, however, to know how to handle their flirting. She nodded and smiled and wove in between their outstretched hands. Yet not one glance in Jake's direction.

For the first time since he had been coming to the inn, he had to put his hand in his pocket to pay for his drink, and he actually ordered an entire bottle of rum. The landlord felt sorry for him as he got steadily more morose and more drunk. 'Come on, old fellow; home with you. His Majesty's Navy have to be served first, you know. Rosie will talk to you in the morning.'

Very carefully, Jake launched himself unsteadily to his feet. Still belching, he managed to get out the door and walk towards

Pig Foot Green without stumbling. Then, just as he rounded the corner, he tripped over a pail of food left out for the pigs that lived there. Something rolled between his feet. Round and round the object went until he suddenly reached down and picked it up gingerly. It was an acorn!

'Hearts of oak, that's what we need!' he shouted to the moon.

A window opened on his left-hand side and a shrill voice shouted, 'Shut your mouth, you old fool.' He felt a broom sticking in his back. The acorn went up in the air and came down into his open mouth. He staggered forward and found he was making his way to the green by the village duck pond. He felt like his heart was cracking open and fell on his back in pain.

It was much later the next day that they found his body. Rosie raced to his side and sobbed. The vicar bent his head and read one of his sweetest poems:

> Sweet, oh sweet is that sensation
> Where two hearts in union meet;
> But the pain of separation
> Mingles bitter with the sweet.

The girl looked at all the villagers staring at her and said loudly, 'He had a fine heart!'

They did not bury his body in the churchyard. He was too much of a villain for that. They left him on the green, buried under garlands of meadowsweet. They never pointed out to the girl the sapling that grew from that spot, but there are plenty today who stop by that magnificent oak growing by the pond at Fingringhoe and remember that a pirate's heart may well have been the best place to plant an acorn.

~ A Strange Funeral ~

Now, you always think of smugglers as men, but Leigh-on-Sea boasted a fine lady smuggler. If you were to see Elizabeth Little at one of her elegant parties in the most refined of company, you would never guess that she dabbled in contraband goods. In her genteel draper's shop there was silk and lace, perfume and gin. Truth to tell, much of those goods were contraband. Elizabeth was involved in the smuggling trade functioning out of Leigh-on-Sea in the 1840s, and did not just organise the business side of things but frequently sailed to the Continent on smuggling expeditions with her two brothers. She quickly proved herself perfectly at ease handling a boat and its crew.

Let me tell you about the one occasion, however, when she nearly got herself into trouble. It began with a blunder. She and her crew were late leaving Ostend, which meant they reached the Thames with the tide against them and, to make matters worse, there was a coastguard cutter in wait for them. Quickly they hoisted more sail and, as they say, more haste less speed. In the process, Elizabeth's brother Bob was wounded in the arm. There was nothing for it but to go for the shallow waters of Shoebury Point and Barling Creek. The crew quickly told Elizabeth it was a bad decision. 'When the tide goes out, we're going to be stranded like rats in a trap with poor old Bob and all the stuff aboard.'

Quick as a flash, Miss Elizabeth came up with a plan. 'Some of you boys are going to take Bob and all the stuff overland, while the rest of you are going to sail the empty boat right under their noses and take it back to Leigh.'

The plan was even more complicated, but she didn't tell the men everything all at once. She just sent William to a Mr Benniworth, the local undertaker, for a horse and carriage. Then the crew realised what she was doing. Bob was put in the coffin and the smuggled goods were all laid out on the floor of the hearse. To make it more convincing, Elizabeth seated herself at the front of the carriage huddled in a black shawl, and sobbed into a fine lace handkerchief.

Nearly everyone they met bent their heads respectfully as the hearse passed. Only when they neared Eden Lodge was there a nasty moment. A customs officer was standing there. The undertaker went pale. He was sure he was about to be arrested, but the customs officer raised his hat and lowered his eyes as a mark of respect. It was almost more than the undertaker could bear. He held his handkerchief tightly to his mouth to stifle his laughter.

That night, when the empty boat came into harbour with William, the whole family were able to celebrate with the finest of French brandies. Bob's wounds had been attended to, the hearse put away in the stable at the back of the house, and nobody was any the wiser about the strange double life of the elegant draper.

⁓ THE KING OF SMUGGLERS ⁓

It was hard to find Paglesham down that narrow, winding road that led to the river. It was always a bit of an adventure and just the right place for a little smuggling. In fact, they do say that the man who was given the title 'Essex's king of smugglers' was a Paglesham man, called William Bligh. He was one of many, but the stories connected with him were always worth the telling.

Like all our folk heroes, William led a double life. Superficially he was a respectable man. He was the village shopkeeper and churchwarden, but it was noticed even there that he had a few odd habits. He wrapped his groceries in the pages of the parish books and other church records! It was, however, at night that he came into his own ... then it was rum and brandy and bales of silk, my hearties, smuggled in the cutter the *Big Jane* all the way from France. What better place to hide them than up the church tower or in the hollowed elms they call 'owd widows' by Pound Pond? Quite a little fortune used to be hidden there I can tell you.

Of course, the revenue men were not completely daft. They would wait around to give chase to *Big Jane*, but those Paglesham men had plenty of tricks up their sleeves. Do you know, on one occasion the commander of a customs cruiser confiscated a cargo of brandy, but William didn't seem the slightest bit bothered.

'Have a drink!' he said to the captain and his crew. It was good French brandy and went down well. Songs were sung and arms waved. 'Have another drink!' William said. And so they did, and another and another. Eventually the Paglesham men left with much cheering, with the customs men totally unaware of what had been happening during their drinking spree. As the kegs had been loaded onto the customs cruiser, the smugglers had passed them back to *Big Jane*. By the time the revenue men left, the smugglers had not only got their own cargo back, but had acquired several casks that the revenue men had confiscated from another smuggling vessel!

As you can guess, this did not endear William to the revenue men. He made a considerable enemy of Mr Loten, the customs officer at Leigh. Imagine Mr Loten's delight when he managed to capture old 'Hard Apple', as William Bligh was nicknamed. He flung Hard Apple into the hold, tied hand and foot. Then, of all things, the ship ran aground on the Goodwin Sands! Things were looking mighty dangerous. There was a real risk that the ship could break up. Loten, in desperation, ran down to the hold and begged for the smuggler's help.

'What do I care if your rotten hulk floats or sinks? I know well enough what you have planned for me. I can tell you I'd rather drown than go to the gallows.'

Loten thought it through and promised William his freedom if he could get the boat off the sands. Of course he could, and the boat was soon out in deep water. Loten, to do him credit, kept his word and let Hard Apple go when they reached land.

The excisemen respected him for his seamanship and his smuggler friends admired his acts of bravado. It was said that he could drink a whole keg of brandy, and they tittered when he crunched and swallowed a wine glass, but the story that was repeated most often was the story of the cricket match.

Now, you would expect a cricket match to be a peaceful occasion for when the smugglers were off duty, but this game resulted in quite the drama. The smugglers were playing in Church Field where the bull was kept. The bull was not pleased to see intruders. One great bellow and the creature came charging across the grass with his head down. The men did not hesitate and made for the gate as fast as they could.

William Bligh, however, was made of sterner stuff. He faced the bull and yelled at it: 'Body and bones. Don't think to frighten me!' He grabbed a cudgel, held the animal by the tail and gave it a good beating. Terrified, the bull tried to shake off its tormenter, but Hard Apple was determined and clung on to the poor animal's tail in a wild chase over hedges and ditches until eventually it fell down dead.

Strangely enough, William Bligh lived to the ripe old age of seventy-four and was buried in Paglesham Church's graveyard. On his deathbed he asked his neighbour for a Bible reading, then sighed, and his last words were, 'Thank you. Now I am ready for the launch.' Well, maybe … hard to know what St Peter would make of such a rascal if he ever got as far as the pearly gates.

~ THE BEST OF THE SMUGGLERS' TRICKS ~

Wherever you stop on the East Coast for a drink in one of the numerous pubs, you are bound to be told a smuggler's yarn. Most coastal villages seem to be honeycombed with tunnels, usually ending in the cellar of a pub to which contraband was once transported. There are ghost stories galore to keep strangers away from investigating the smugglers' hiding places, and so many jokes and tricks at the expense of the customs men. Here are some of the best.

Ghostly Wagons at Great Stambridge

Oh! There were such tales of the ghost wagon that haunted the land between the Crouch and the Roach. It was a fearsome thing, for it passed through without as much as the creak of a wheel or the clop of a horse's hoof. It sent folk scurrying indoors to the safe haven of their fireplaces. Yet here is the truth of it. It was only a smuggler greeting the arrival of contraband goods at Stambridge, with a cart whose wheels were covered with thick cloth and the hooves of the horses covered in sponge. Eventually the excisemen did catch most of the Stamford Gang, except, strangely enough, the owner of the 'ghost bus' himself, who appears to have been a Mr Moss.

Female Wiles at Harwich

Excisemen had their weaknesses, as a lady innkeeper at Harwich discovered. Her feminine wiles were enough to send the tide surveyor reeling. When he arrived at her establishment, he realised that she appeared to have something concealed in her stays. Laughing, she took him round the neck and held him and kissed him a considerable time in the presence of several people. It is said that when a Mr Orlibar and a Mr Pelham went to see her in the public house known as the Three Cups, and told her that she had some prohibited goods concealed about her, she immediately lifted her petticoats up to her waist. No doubt this was a very effective way of distracting them from their work!

The Brandy Cupboard in Great Bentley

In the house known as Palfreyman's in Great Bentley there was a cupboard known as the brandy cupboard. Its door was visible to anybody walking into the room, and even after opening this door it would seem to be a perfectly conventional china cupboard. If, however, you moved the china, you would find another door which was a wonderful hiding hole for contraband brandy. Now, in case you think I have made this story up, as I have been known to do, the local doctor's groom had a son who remembered quite clearly what used to happen when he was a little boy. He and his father were often told to take a horse and cart to Alresford Creek. The cart was loaded with hay and the child was given a turnip to eat to keep him quiet. He was told not to speak to anybody on any account, or to watch what was happening. Boys will be boys, however, and he did see quite clearly what happened when they got to the creek – some hay was removed and replaced with a keg of brandy! When they got home to Palfreyman's the alcohol was put in the hiding place in the cupboard, and rumour had it that it was shared by the doctor and the parson!

Rascals of Rowhedge

If you want to see the face of a real rogue, take a look at the photograph of Jack Spitty, a Rowhedge smack owner, smuggler and licensee of the Royal Oak. Underneath his sou'wester is a villainous face decorated with a fringe of a beard, a sly smile and a tangle of wrinkles around dark, laughing eyes. His favourite way to hide his smuggled Dutch cigars was to build them into the shape of a dressing table and cover them with chintz cloth, a mirror and various dressing table accessories. His favourite expression was: 'If you were born to be drowned, you won't be hanged'! He was, in fact, a very brave sailor. On one occasion his smack was caught in a severe gale in the North Sea. He set a storm jib, sent the crew down below, and took the helm himself. A big wave washed him overboard but the next one washed him back. When the crew finally came up on deck they found they were off to Heligoland!

The best hiding place was surely when smugglers hid their goods under the bed of an old man who was dying. The revenue men peeped round his door, saw the sick man propped up on his pillows, and left him alone. The old man died happy, knowing that he had outwitted the revenue men with his last breath. That was how it was in Rowhedge. They were proud of their smugglers in those days and I have met many families who still are today!

~ THE HIGHWAYMAN AND THE FAIRIES ~

'Well, what are you doing, my man?' a voice boomed from above Stephen Bunce. Slyly, Bunce looked up and saw a gentleman seated on a handsome horse; then suddenly he threw himself to the ground and lay there, apparently listening to something that came from within the earth itself. The gentleman was amazed and moved closer to the recumbent figure. There seemed to be no reaction. 'Answer me, you fool!'

'Shh … !'

'What is it? What are you hearing?'

A blissful expression came over Stephen Bunce's face. 'Fairies. I can hear fairies. It's the most beautiful sound I ever head. Such sweet music!'

Well, in our day and age we would expect nothing but laughter from the gentleman, but this was 1707 and in 1707 people in Essex believed in house elves, imps and fairies of all sorts. The gentleman wanted to know more. He could not resist it. He dismounted from his horse and gave Bunce the reins to hold while he put his own ear to the ground. Of course there was nothing! Nothing, that is, except the thumping of a horse's hooves galloping away. Bunce was riding the gentleman's horse to Romford.

A highwayman always knows a fine horse when he sees one. So, for that matter, does an innkeeper. The landlord of the inn where Bunce had stopped recognised the black stallion as soon as he saw it. 'That's Mr Bartlett's horse.'

'So it is, so it is. Mr Bartlett has asked me to offer him as a pledge, for he's asking you kindly, sir, if you could lend him fifteen guineas. It's a little matter of a debt of honour at Ingatestone, you understand.'

The landlord understood quickly enough. Mr Bartlett was a notorious gambler. The horse was a good bargain in the circumstances and he handed over fifteen guineas in a leather bag to Bunce without a protest. The highwayman, for a moment, had trouble keeping his face straight but he marched away happily with his loot. It was just as well he was not there when Mr Bartlett finally arrived at the inn. Sadly, we have no record of what he said when the innkeeper told him: 'There was no need to have left the horse. I would have lent you the money anyway …'

Sometimes a donkey was good enough for Bunce's purposes. It so happened that one fair day Bunce was walking up a hill near Romford with a friend when they came upon an old farmer absentmindedly leading a donkey. The old man's mind was on the fine supper he was expecting that night. Bunce crept up very quietly to the donkey, took off its bridle and put it over his own head, while his friend made off with the donkey.

At the top of the hill, the old man went to mount his donkey. Can you imagine his amazement when he saw a man instead of his faithful donkey? Bunce could see he was shocked, and quickly explained that he was a man who had committed a terrible sin and as a result he had been turned into a donkey. 'And now I have atoned for my sin and am a man again.'

'And as a man you should return to your family!' The old farmer let him go.

The next day the old farmer hunted out a new donkey in the local market. Bunce, of course, had not missed a trick. He had sold the donkey on for a good price and it was up for resale. When the old man saw his beast again, he shook his head sadly and said, 'What? Committed another sin already? I shan't buy you again!'

How sad that Bunce himself did not learn his lesson. He could not stop thieving and was hanged at Tyburn not long after that.

⚊ Sixteen-String Jack ⚊

Ellen, the innkeeper, loved him dearly despite his weaknesses. After all, was there ever a highwayman with more panache than Sixteen-String Jack? You've not heard of him? Then listen to this tale. His real name was John Rann, but everybody called him Sixteen-String Jack. How had he come by such a nickname? Well, as every barmaid in Essex in those days could tell you, this came about because of the sixteen coloured ribbons that were tied to the knees of his breeches. Wherever he went, he cut a dashing figure – even at the most fashionable balls and parties in London.

It took a considerable number of shillings to maintain such a sense of fashion. So how was it done? Ellen knew, but she kept mum. Sometimes Jack would pick a pocket on the Hounslow Road. Sometimes Jack would ride into Epping Forest for a little highway robbery. Always, he managed to get out of trouble. Six times he was brought before the court before he was finally found guilty. Had he listened to Ellen, he might have been saved even then. His appearances at court were certainly spectacular. On one occasion he appeared with bright blue bows tied to his leg irons, and in his buttonhole was a bunch of flowers as large as a birch broom.

On one of Jack and Ellen's outings to the countryside, Jack swept into the room with such a flourish of his lace hat that the assembled company rose to their feet in appreciation of his elegant appearance! With a wave of his hand, he settled the company down for a serious evening's drinking. Foolish man, the wine flowed liberally. No sooner had Jack downed his first bottle of wine, he lifted his glass to propose a toast to all highwaymen. To make matters worse, he added brightly, 'For I am one myself.' His eyes twinkled. The room felt silent.

The company were thoroughly alarmed. Jack turned to the old lady in the high white wig by his side and patted her on her hand. 'But you need not worry, for tonight I am making holiday.'

Even in his befuddlement, Jack noticed later in the evening that he had lost a diamond ring from his hand. There was another awkward silence, then the smile was back on his lips. He hiccoughed. 'It was nothing, nothing at all. Only worth a paltry £100, less than a lazy evening's work. I'll let this trifling thieving pass.'

By now the atmosphere had completely changed. He was no longer the object of admiration but someone to be distrusted. The assembled company would have no more of him. They pushed him through the window! Ellen was outraged. There were seventeen of those blackguards to just one of her Jack. She scratched out at the face of the nearest grandee and ran out to join Jack on his trip back to Convent Garden.

Inevitably, such casualness about money meant funds were getting low after so many stylish outings. Jack was more often on the road, with less and less to show for it. Ellen was canny enough to realise the danger of stealing watches. She was always saying to him, 'Jack, take all the money you can. Guineas tell no tales. But leave the watches in their owner's fob.' And it was a watch that was to be his downfall.

In 1774 he was on the road when he stopped a Dr Bell, no less a person than the chaplain to the Princess Amelia. Jack just shouted, 'Give me your money and take no notice or I'll have your brains out.' The clergyman gave him eighteen pence. Eighteen pence! What an insult! Jack was forced to take the parson's watch and trinkets as well.

Ellen foolishly took the watch to the pawnbroker. The pawnbroker took the watch to the owner. Jack and Ellen found themselves the next day at the court in the Old Bailey. Jack's presence seemed to light up that hot, stifling place and, as they left the court, it appeared they were being followed by a guard of honour made up of a thousand people. Jack took to all of this attention like an actor, and he was even more splendidly dressed than usual. His coat and waistcoat were of pea-green cloth; his buckskin breeches were spotlessly new, and all tricked out with his famous strings; his hat was bound round with silver cords.

After a month, Jack and Ellen stood together in the dock for the judge's final verdict. As they stood there, he whispered, 'Cheer up my girl. I have ordered the best supper that Covent Garden could provide and we will make merry tonight when this foolish old judge has done his duty.'

Ellen never had that supper. She never saw her Jack again. On 30 November 1774, John Rann was hanged at Tyburn. His last words were that the gallows were something he had 'long expected to see'. Rumour had it that he had seven merry girls to keep him company on his last night in the prison cell at Newgate, and that he laughed even to the end, although he had hoped for a last-minute rescue. But then, being the Essex boy he was, he would, wouldn't he?

— Dick Turpin's Last Rant —

(An original sheet ballad published in 1739)

Bold Turpin was ariding one day on the moor,
He saw a noble lawyer go ariding before,
Turpin he rode and to him did say
How often did you see Bold Turpin ride this way?
For I'm the hero, I am the great Turpin Ho

Now say Turpin for to be artful
My money I have hid in my boot
And now says the Lawyer a man cannot find
I hid my money in my cape coat behind.
For I'm the hero, I am the great Turpin Ho.

They rode together and came to a mill,
Turpin bid the lawyer to stand still
Take off your coat, it must come off
My horse is in want of a saddle cloth.
For I'm the hero, I am the great Turpin Ho.

Now Turpin has robbed him of all his store,
And when that has gone, he knows where to get more,
And the very first town that you came in
Tell him you've been robbed by Bold Turpin
For I'm the hero, I am the great Turpin.

Now Turpin is caught
And for a game cock he was hung at last
A hundred pounds he lay there aside
All for Jack Ketch his legacy
For I'm the hero, I'm the great Turpin Ho.

~ BLACK BESS ~

Black Bess did not exist. There, I've said it! She was mentioned in an early nineteenth-century ballad, but the famous ride to York was added to the Victorian novel *Rookwood* by William Harrison Ainsworth. This novel, in its time, outsold Dickens. So it is a storyteller's tale which outlives the truth, so let us celebrate good Black Bess.

Black Bess's sire was a desert Arabian brought to this country by a wealthy traveller. Her dam was a coal-black English racer. Bess's coat was so black that it was like polished jet without a single white hair. She had an elegant little head and was built more for strength than beauty. Her temperament was so gentle that she could be ridden by a child.

The ride to York began after the mistaken shooting of a Tom King, Turpin's fellow highwayman. Turpin decided to set out from Kilburn to York to avoid the posse chasing him. Amongst her achievements, Bess jumped a tollgate at Hornsey. When she started to flag, Dick rubbed her down with a solution of water and brandy and then swam her across the river Ouse. Then, sadly, a mile out of the city of York, she collapsed.

Bess tottered and fell. There was a terrible gasp – a parting moan – a snort; her eye gazed, for an instant, upon her master, with a dying glare: then grew glassy rayless and fixed. A shiver ran through her frame. Her heart had burst.

Ah! Here then is a true heroine.

~ THE WIDOW'S RANT ~

Rant and rage, rant and rage
As the Widow rides and rides
Down, down, Trap Hill,
Down, down the Essex road to Hell
Behind the great Turpin O!
The Turpin O who whelped a napper
And croaked a Toby Man
And stole the widow Shelley's mite.

You've not heard those expressions then? They are old thieves' slang. To whelp a napper means to be born a thief, and to croak a Toby Man is to die a highwayman. Yes, that was the truth of Dick Turpin's life. As for the widow, Mrs Shelley was one of the countless victims of the Essex Gang.

Now, if you live in Loughton, you will know that there is a strange ghost story linking Dick Turpin and the widow Shelley. The two ghosts are said to appear at Traps Hill, Loughton, three times a year. The shade of Dick Turpin comes galloping down the hill on his horse like a man possessed. Suddenly, from behind a lime tree at a farm gate, the wraith of an old woman appears. She seems nothing but a bundle of bones yet manages to leap onto his horse. Clinging onto Turpin's waist, she points with her skinny finger and howls the names of the places they must visit.

First they must stop at the widow Shelley's own farm. It's an isolated place and the widow whispers in his ear: 'See, this is where it all began one Saturday night; that's when you and the gang burst in through my door. There were five of you scoundrels and you grabbed me and my poor young maid and blindfolded us with handkerchiefs. And then I heard you say, "What money is in the house?" I wouldn't say. "I'll put you on the fire if you don't tell me." I hesitated, but you did not. You picked me up in your butcher's arms and carried me over to the fire and there held me above the flames! I smell the burning fabric of my skirt even now, and as for the pain …' Her voice turns to howls again. She knows what that pain did to her. She told the villains where her money was and they took it all, all her life's savings, and truth to tell it was no widow's mite but a small fortune.

It is the nature of the curse that Turpin must keep moving, and the widow points out the direction they must go with her skinny finger. Their next destination is Edgware in Middlesex. It is another isolated farm. Turpin stops shivering at the gate. He remembers that it was here the gang dismounted at 7 p.m. one evening when most of the farm labourers were being dismissed for the day. They found a shepherd boy returned from folding his sheep. Threatening the boy with a pistol, they took off his garters, tied his hands, and told him to knock on the door to summon the servants. When he got as far as the door, the boy could barely speak for terror.

So in the end the gang knocked on the door themselves and were lucky enough not to be questioned, just mistaken for the neighbours. There was no hesitation. In they rushed, shouting and flourishing their pistols. There sat the owner, a man of seventy, motionless with fear. The gang ransacked the house. Turpin concentrated on seeing what information he could get out of the old man. He pulled his victim's breeches round his ankles to stop him running away and took all the coins from the pockets. This was a wealthy house then. Where was the rest of his money? He refused to tell them.

Turpin beat the old man's bare buttocks, while the rest of the gang beat him about the head with their pistols. More threats of murder. One of the gang picked up a kettle of water from over the fire and threw it over the old man, but fortunately it was not boiling.

Of course, it was the business with the maid that shocked the public most when the story got to the broadsheets. One of the maidservants was in the dairy churning butter when she heard the noise from the house. She suspected something was wrong and blew out her candle. Unluckily for the poor girl, she walked straight into Samuel Gregory, the gang's leader, who led her up to the garrets and there raped her at pistol point. It was of no significance, Turpin thought. The gang finished robbing, locked the family in the parlour and threw the key away.

'So you remember it all, you dog,' the widow beats upon his shoulders. 'Then ride on and let us visit the farm of Mr Francis at Mary-le-Bone.' Again a place of isolation, and in the driveway a fine cow-house in which to bind and imprison two servants and the master himself. Yet what drives the widow into more ranting and raging is to hear of the treatment of the mistress of the house, for she was hit with the butt of a whip until blood poured down her face. Much of what was stolen was only of sentimental value. The widow howls in triumph. 'Too far! You went too far. The gang get caught, your highwayman friend dies and you mount the gallows to swing.'

'The gallows did not frighten me, old woman. They came in crowds to see me die and I bowed to them all. Even when my leg trembled as I ascended to the fatal tree, I kept my calm.'

❧

'Ah, but see how it is with you now. You are my prisoner and you must ride with me to eternity so all may know your true self. All may understand the crimes you have committed. See how the faces change to hatred when they hear your name now. No more the hero! We will ride and ride through Essex and all will hear what you have done.'

And should you encounter the ghastly figures of the widow and Turpin riding through the dust of an Essex road late at night, and hear the widow's howls, then you will shudder at the man who whelped a napper and croaked a Toby Man and stole the widow Shelley's mite.

Dick Turpin was convicted of horse stealing and was hanged on Saturday 7 April 1739. He was apprehended while wantonly shooting one of his landlord's fowls, and his conviction was made possible because his brother refused to pay sixpence for the postage of a letter from him.

~ THE HORSE WITH NO EARS ~

Leigh House used to stand high above the busy harbour of Leigh-on-Sea. It had the most splendid views of that quaint little town. By 1751, however, it had been unoccupied for years and, like all unoccupied houses, had fallen into the most dreadful decay – rats and overgrown greenery everywhere; yet there was news that a stranger was taking an interest in rebuilding the ruins …

It was Nancy Smith, the barmaid from the Crooked Billet, who first got wind of the stranger. She was used to passing

Leigh House on the way to visiting her widowed mother. 'I saw him go in the house I tell you. He had a key for it; although the door was that rotten, it practically fell apart with the first touch.'

'What sort of fellow is he?' You had to be careful with strangers. Times were hard and even an odd bit of smuggling was hard to come by.

'Well, I tell you, he's far from handsome. He's built just like a prize bulldog with a coarse red face and a squint. I tell you he had a fine pair of pistols in his belt. And as for his horse, I've never seen a more peculiar creature! A strong brown mare, well set on good legs but with no ears!'

'No ears!' The whole bar laughed at such a thing but Thomas Arkwright, who came from Hadleigh, looked a little thoughtful. That very day he'd seen a man ride through Hadleigh at lightning speed, splashed up to his wig in mud. He had looked very like the man the girl had described, but his horse had had ears. Thomas never said anything. He did not want to embarrass the girl any more. She was still flushed with annoyance at the men's reaction. They were beginning to make jokes about horses with four tails and the rider having horns and a tail.

Mind you, as time passed the bricklayers and carpenters who were employed by the new owner of Leigh House must have wondered if they were working for the Devil himself, for he was the worst tempered of men and so mean. His name was Mr Craddock. The fact that Nancy had been right about him riding a horse with no ears called Meg was barely mentioned. It was just another sign of a man who would always get a bargain. No doubt Meg had been bought cheap in the market.

Mr Craddock seemed to want to move into the house quickly, for he planned to marry in the summer. The rector said he was a gentleman of education and breeding who could play an impressive game of chess.

The workmen made little effort to produce their best work. Their real irritation was that their employer was so mean with the beer. Even on the very day when the last beam was set in place in the roof – usually such a grand excuse for a party – there was not a drop of drink. Rumour spread that the master had been furious at the men when they had asked for their beer. 'Beer! You want beer? Well, if you're thirsty, you varlets, there's the pond for you. Lap the water like the lazy dogs you are.' And on and on he went with his string of swear words until the men crept away like whipped hounds.

The story went round the town until some merry fellow rechristened the house Lapwater Hall. That would teach him to tell Leigh men to drink water. It hardly amused Mr Craddock to have his fine house so degraded. He would as soon knock a man down as hear him call his fine new mansion such a name! In fact, it was said that when he walked into the pub called the Smack, he took his whip to Sam Gillson for having the audacity to laugh in his face.

Even when his maidservant accidentally referred to the house as Lapwater Hall, Craddock's rage knew no bounds. 'They shan't give my house that name for nothing. By God, if anyone drinks ought but water here, I'll take it back with a carving knife.' He stormed off and turned the key in the cellar door, and put it in his pocket where it remained.

There was other talk too. The master would disappear for days at a time and then come home, lock himself in his room and drink all day. He had no friends it seemed – as might be expected of a person who is ungenerous with his drink. No one knew where his wealth came from. He had certainly not been seen out on the boats with the smugglers.

The answer came one night later in the winter. Nancy Smith's mother had taken employment at Lapwater Hall as a cook and, on this particular night, the master had gone out. It was well after midnight, and the woman was glad that her daughter had called in to keep her company. It was a dark night with a thin sliver of a moon and the wind was rising. The two women could not get rid of the feeling that something was wrong. The dog was restless in the yard and rattled its chain. It howled like the hound of death. There was the sound of a horse's hooves but it was the uneven rhythm of a horse that has been lamed. Then the door was flung open and the master practically fell into the room. 'Quick! Give me your apron, woman.' He grabbed Nan's apron and wrapped it tightly around his bleeding arm, then drank hard from a jug of water. 'Put out the lights,' he growled, 'and bolt the door after me when I go out.'

He left and then they heard the pounding at the door. The women clung to each other for dear life, but the pounding went on. Voices shouted, 'Open in the name of the King!' Nancy looked out of the window and saw it was a group of officers. It was best not to argue. She let them in and soon the house was full of light as the officers searched. One of the younger men noticed the women's frightened faces. 'We're looking for Cutler Lynch, the highwayman. Have you seen him?'

'What does he look like?'

'It's said he's far from handsome. He's built just like a prize bulldog with a coarse red face and a squint, and he had a fine pair of pistols in his belt.'

Nancy almost nodded. Then she said, 'And his horse has no ears …'

The men gave her a funny look. 'I don't know what you mean but that horse the Cutler rides has spirit and a fine pair of ears. We've ridden after him through Shenfield, where he shot a man and then got a bullet through his own arm. We rode through Ingrave, Laindon and Pitsea and the Benfleet Marshes and still that horse rode on. It seemed to know every step of the way but it was winded when we got here.'

They all went out to see where the mare might have got to, and found her by the pond. A hat was floating on the water. The men took a rake and hauled it in and then they saw the body of the dead highwayman staring up at them. Obviously he had hidden in the reeds until loss of blood had made him faint and he had drowned. It was Nancy who noticed something else in the water. It was the strangest thing! It was a pair of horse's ears joined by a strap and fitted with a catch to hold to the headstall. Then they all looked at each other and realised how Cutler had led his double life. Craddock, as the gentleman, had ridden his earless horse; but Cutler the highwayman could not afford to stand out, and had put the false ears over Meg's head.

The young officer led the mare closer to the water and let her drink. She was thirsty. She at least had a right to drink at Lapwater Hall. She had served her master so faithfully that now she could barely stand.

Four

THE DISCOVERY OF WITCHES

One of the strangest features of Essex is the enormous number of witchcraft stories. Five-hundred-and-fifty people were accused of witchcraft in Essex between 1560 and 1680, with 100 sentenced to the hangman's noose, most of them old women. Chelmsford hanged more witches than anywhere else in England.

Whatever was going on? Sylvia Kent, in her book *Folklore of Essex*, paints a picture of tiny, isolated villages populated by illiterate people who were continually plagued by anxieties about the loss of crops and livestock, bad weather, illnesses for which there was no explanation and, of course, the death of babies. Who could be blamed? For so many, it was easiest to point the finger at that defenceless, poverty-stricken old woman who lived on her own with no man to defend her.

In recent times there has been a more vigorous attempt to reach a genuine understanding of what was really taking place. Historians like Malcolm Gaskill, in *Witchfinders: A Seventeenth-Century English Tragedy*, have examined the evidence more carefully and shown how vulnerable old women were. An example of this awakened sensibility to the persecution of the time are the posies of flowers left at the gate of Colchester Castle recently, as a memorial to the women imprisoned there as witches in 1645.

During the Tudor period there was a flood of witch trials, including one in 1566 involving three women from Hatfield Peverel whose lives had been destroyed by a wicked white cat! No one at the time seemed at all surprised at this. In 1582, St Osyth was the village where women seemed to be continually blaming each other for agricultural disasters or family tragedies. Justice Darcy of St Clere Hall, who was the local witch hunter, landowner and magistrate, took advantage of their peevish quarrels and brought the women to court on charges of witchcraft.

In 1921, witchcraft surfaced again in the village when the skeletons of two supposed sixteenth-century witches were dug up in a garden.

The most notorious witch hunts were those conducted by a young Manningtree lawyer called Matthew Hopkins with the assistance of John Stearne, a Puritan landowner. He could not have done what he did at any other time in history. In 1645, the world turned upside down as England plunged into Civil War and the final effects of religious division stirred up hatred in even the smallest of communities.

Hopkins' first visit to the house of Elizabeth Clarke is an episode luridly depicted in the woodcut of Hopkins' booklet 'The Discovery of Witches'. It shows him surrounded by the witches and the most grotesque animals, obviously familiars. The local magistrate, Sir Harbottle Grimston, had sent Stearne and Hopkins to question the one-legged beggar woman about the death of a tailor's wife, supposedly caused by witchcraft, and what happened then is the most dramatic of stories and almost incomprehensible to our modern sensibilities.

The fate of Rebecca West, the youngest of the Manningtree witches to be accused, is a bit of a mystery. Shockingly, she gave evidence against her mother and the other women and then curiously disappeared without a record of a plea or a verdict at the trial. Was the fact that Hopkins visited her alone at night when she was imprisoned in Colchester Castle significant? Betty Potter of Boxted had her own special way of escaping the alarming Mr Hopkins.

Strangely enough, the idea of magical powers did not completely disappear even in the nineteenth century, although then it centred mainly on the 'cunning men' who cured your warts and found your missing objects. Only the tale of the sea-witch Sarah Moore contains echoes of the old fears.

There is no need to embellish these tales. The voices of the past cry out and speak for themselves. I felt I had to add something a little lighter to end the section and found inspiration in H. Cranmer-Byng's story of the mawkin.

⚊ THE WICKED WHITE CAT ⚊

It all began when Elizabeth was twelve years old and her grandmother taught her to become a witch. To help her with her magic, Elizabeth was given a white spotted cat, suitably called Satan. He was looked after well in a comfortable basket and fed with milk and bread. He was grateful and asked his mistress in a hollow voice, 'What do you want in life?'

'Riches!'

Like many folk of her time, she believed riches could be made from wool, and so Satan gave her twenty-eight sheep. But whether she was a bad shepherdess or whether Satan was whimsical with his gifts, the sheep vanished.

'And who do you want to marry?'

'Andrew Byles.'

The cat advised that she lay with Andrew first. It turned out to be bad advice. She got pregnant and Andrew refused to marry her. This decided her. It was easy enough to lose the child with the help of devilish magic. Satan gave his instructions and the child was aborted with the use of herbs. Not long after that, Andrew Byles' business failed and he died of grief.

It was best for Elizabeth to find another husband for herself. She found a Mr Francis and the couple had a daughter. Fifteen years on, however, Elizabeth was still not happy. It was what was known as an 'unquiet' marriage. There was a great deal of swearing and cursing in that house. Her daughter died and her husband became lame. His lameness, it seemed, was caused by Satan changing himself into a toad and leaping into the man's shoes.

The cat had done its work and Elizabeth was growing weary of him. She gave the cat to her sister Agnes Waterson in exchange for a cake. Agnes, always quarrelsome, now found herself falling out with her neighbours. Satan was able to help her keep a power over them – drown a cow, kill three pigs and three geese, let brewing and butter making be ruined and let her husband die. Satan, meanwhile, was living well on scraps of chicken, but even he had his problems. Agnes could not afford to keep the cat's basket lined with soft wool, so she had him changed into a toad that lived in a pot.

But Satan had even more tricks in his new guise. Agnes's daughter was hungry and begged bread and cheese from her neighbour. Her request was refused. Never, never refuse a witch anything! Satan now transformed himself into a more hideous form. According to the hysterical girl, the creature that appeared to her was like a black dog with an ape's face, a short tail, a chain and a silver whistle about his neck, a pair of horns on his head and, carrying in his mouth, the key of the milk house door. He terrified her, demanding butter and bringing into the house all sorts of things from the outside world, including a knife.

As you can imagine, all of this was more than the neighbours could stand and they gave their evidence in court. The three women were found to be witches and were finally hanged in 1566.

And what of Satan? Oh, you won't see him on the streets of Hatfield Peverel today. He can still visit us in our nightmares, though, in one of his many shape-shifting disguises. Beware! He is at his most dangerous when he comes lolloping through our nightmares as a large white spotted cat.

~ SKELETON HOUSE ~

In 1582 St Osyth was abuzz. Justice Darcy of St Clere Hall was sniffing out 'the pestilent people', those witches mentioned in the good Queen Elizabeth's new laws. His task was easy for here was a community filled with spite and fear. Accusations were everywhere. It was said that old women could barely move through lameness due to witches' curses. There were strange rituals with hog dung and herbs. Brewings of beer and batches of bread had gone bad, and a whole barn of corn went up in flames because of evil spells.

At the centre of the drama was a woman called Ursula Kemp. She had earned her living as a midwife, wet nurse and herbal healer. Then a neighbour rejected her services and that woman's baby fell from a cradle. A curse, no doubt, the village all said. Then they heard her mutter odd things at another neighbour's daughter, who fell ill and died. Witchcraft was involved, they were sure.

Why, even Ursula's illegitimate eight-year-old son told tales against his mother! He claimed that she kept 'familiars' and that she was responsible for the death of Elizabeth Stratton. It was no surprise to the villagers then when she admitted to these crimes and named other women whom she believed to be witches. Some of the accused were acquitted, but not Ursula. She was hanged and buried according to the custom with witches, with rivets driven through her elbows and knees. This, it was said, would prevent her rising from the ground.

Time passed and time passed. These tales of malice and horror seemed to fade away and then, in 1921, St Osyth was abuzz again. Workmen digging sand hit something hard, and to their horror found it was a pair of skeletons, just 6ft below the surface. The skeletons had not been put in a coffin and had iron rivets placed in their knees and elbows. So here again was the sign of witchcraft! This was a shock – the witches of St Osyth had long been forgotten.

Mr Brooker, who owned the cottage with the garden where the skeletons were dug up, decided to take advantage of such sinister goings-on. He made his cottage a tourist attraction, charging admission and selling postcards of the 'witches'. The cottage became known as Skeleton House. He claimed that the two skeletons were in fact Ursula Kemp and Elizabeth Bennet, two women who had been accused of witchcraft in 1582. But there was never any real proof about their identity; their stories were just the most wickedly scandalous. Mr Brooker was doing rather nicely out of the visitors to his garden.

He was, however, to have a nasty shock. One night, not long after the discovery of the skeletons, Skeleton House and three nearby cottages went up in flames. Fortunately, Mr and

Mrs Brooker, their three daughters and son rushed out in their nightclothes just as the roof fell in. Mrs Curtis, an eighty-five-year-old widow, was carried out of her flaming room by three men. Amazingly, the fire did not spread to the rest of the row of timbered houses, despite the fact that the water had to be drawn from a millpond and about quarter of a mile of hose had to be used to keep the fire under control.

Well, whoever the skeletons were, there are people alive today who paid their sixpence to see those skeletons and who still shiver at the thought and reach for a strong drink to drown the memory. I've met one of them, so I know.

Yet what happened to the skeleton of 'Ursula' after the fire? Firstly it was bought by Cecil Williamson at the Witchcraft Museum, Boscastle, who promised that her name would not again be exploited. Then it passed into the ownership of an eccentric artist, a Robert Lenkiewicz, a collector of the occult. When he died, there were arguments about what to do with the skeleton. Fortunately, she found a new champion in a documentary maker called John Worland. He had already made a documentary with the help of the women of Manningtree about the Hopkins persecutions, so he understood what a dreadful tragedy the witchcraft trials represented. He read the documents for the St Osyth trials and this began his campaign to return what was obviously a sixteenth-century skeleton to a peaceful grave in St Osyth.

In 2011 St Osyth was abuzz again. The campaign to give the skeleton a decent burial in an unconsecrated plot of ground in her home village was won. Many people came to the simple ceremony. They came as a gesture of respect for all the women from this town who perished as a result of so malicious a witch hunt. May they rest in peace.

⚊ ENTER MASTER HOPKINS ⚊

On 4 March 1645 a door opened into the hovel of a one-legged, aged beggar woman, and two of the most infamous witchfinders stepped into English history. In the room they entered, respectable members of the community had been sitting and watching the old woman for three nights for any signs of witchcraft. They watched the two cloaked figures enter with apprehension. A chill ran down every spine and hasty prayers were mumbled. They had sat for so long in the semi-darkness that their minds were wild with terrible fears. One of the men could so easily be the Devil himself, the other his servant, come to claim a witch for their evil purposes.

Then the man spoke and there was a sigh of relief. They recognised him as John Stearne, just one of the local gentry. Slinking in behind him came the young lawyer Matthew Hopkins with his greyhound.

They had come to question Elizabeth Clarke about her and any fellow witches in the town. Time after time they asked for names, but she said nothing. Up and down her only room, they marched her. Hobbling on one leg, she tapped her way painfully with her crutch, but not a word. Stearne and Hopkins turned for the door impatiently. There was nothing to be had here. But as they opened the door to leave, Clarke spoke her first words that night, 'I will show you my imps, for they be ready to come.'

Everyone in the room shuffled a little awkwardly. Was it going to happen? Were the devilish familiars going to make their appearance at last after three nights of sleepless waiting?

Elizabeth smiled. 'They will not harm you, be not afraid.'

Matthew Hopkins was not a tall man but his shadow filled the wall as he pointed his finger at her. 'Why do you not fear this Devil's spawn? They mean nothing but evil in this world. Can you not see, old woman, that they could bring grievous harm to you?'

'What! Do you think I be afeard of my own children? Sit and you will see.'

While the whole company turned to face the corner to which she pointed, Edward Parsley, one of the watchers, spoke gently, 'Bess, has the Devil had use of your body?'

'He has. It is true. And he is a tall, proper, black-haired gentleman. A properer man than yourself, Master Hopkins.' She spoke easily of her intimacy with Satan six years earlier. He would arrive in his splendid lace collar and say, 'Bess, I must lie with you.' She would not refuse him. Their lovemaking would last half the night and sometimes even longer. Then suddenly she started to call, 'Holt, Holt, come to me my Holt.' Nothing appeared. Nobody moved.

Then as the gloom grew deeper in that dank place a presence made itself felt. A white creature crept into the room. It was smaller than a cat, yet like one. It greeted its mistress and retreated into the dark. More and more creatures began to appear. There was a dog with very short legs called Jeremiah, a greyhound with very long legs called Vinegar Tom. Toads and ferrets came and went.

'Are there more of these creatures with heathen names?' Hopkins wanted to know.

'Ah, there's Sack and Sugar,' she said, pointing to two black creatures. 'They are angry with you, Mr Stearne, for trying to have me swum. You are lucky they did not jump on your face for they might have squeezed down your throat and deposited a feast of toads in your belly. These are the Devil's imps and they have left their mark on me. All who have these marks are witches and are bound to the Devil. He is a hard master. I did not want to kill Robert Taylor's horse or Farmer Edwards' pigs, yet he would have it so. I have never been able to gainsay him.'

Matthew Hopkins left the room that night sure of his mission. He had heard enough and walked purposefully through the town. In the dark shadows of the street, his greyhound caught a glimpse of a small white creature. It gave chase but strangely could not close in on it. Each time the greyhound came close, the creature seemed to flit from it as easily as a bird from one branch to another. Hopkins peered through the gloom, following the progress of the chase as best he could. Both creatures ran out of sight and a yelp was heard. Within seconds the hound had returned, whimpering and with its shoulder bleeding.

'So she sends one of her imps to frighten me, to put me from my duty to God and the people,' Hopkins muttered. 'But I am not

so easily swayed from the path of righteousness as that Mistress Clarke. Your imps do not frighten me.'

But it was not the last he saw of those satanic creatures for, when he arrived at his lodgings, a large black cat-like creature was sat on his strawberry bed. It fixed Hopkins with a stare and bolted for the gate. The dog gave chase, but soon came back shaking and trembling to the side of its master. Hopkins fondled the dog's ears and whispered confidently, 'I shall be a Witchfinder General in this great realm in the battle against the Evil One and his hordes. I will be known.'

— Rebecca West —

She stood in the doorway of Lawford Church and felt their hatred wrap around her like a shroud.

'Witch and daughter of a witch!'

'See how they sit at sermon, Rebecca and her old crone of a mother, like two of God's own saints but they are nothing but evil, the very servants of Satan.'

'They told us before they came here from Rivenhall that good men and babes were cursed by them.'

And then, loud amongst the chorus of hatred, came the voice of Thomas Hart. 'Her mother was responsible for the death of my sow, and Thomas Cutler lost his son these five years past by Ann West's wickedness.'

Then his wife shrieked louder than all, 'Rebecca looked at me with the evil eye until I was driven from the church in my pain to miscarry my child in the public street. Even last night, as I lay in my bed, something – I know not what – fell upon my right side until I became lame with extraordinary pains and burning. I am in danger and all because this creature thinks me her greatest enemy.'

'She must be questioned.'

It was rector John Ede who questioned her. Thirty years he had laboured in the parish and he had never seen his congregation in such desperation, despite the fact that through God's servants the building was now a proper place of worship with no altar rails, a simple communion table, and the graven images of stone and glass destroyed wherever possible. Rebecca saw in his eyes his fear that, despite everything, the Devil was now loose in his parish, but his voice was gentle and silky and she wanted to please him. She knew how the Devil must work and told the eager clerk how Satan himself had come to her in the shape of a 'marvellous proper man', and in her voice was the longing of a girl who wanted a marvellous proper man to comfort her.

This time it was the justices themselves who listened to her evidence. These were the men of power – Sir Harbottle Grimston and Sir Thomas Bowes. She must give some useful information, for now the shadow of the gallows was above her head and she must not allow herself to be destroyed with these old hags. She recited their names: Elizabeth Clarke, Elizabeth Gooding, Ann Leech and Helen Leech, and she mentioned their meeting and their 'spirits', yet the accusations were not so terrible – garbled tales of men falling off horses, of dead horses and cows, and lame hogs. And then her name had to be mentioned – Ann West, her own mother. Rebecca looked at her feet.

All her mother wanted of her spirits was that she might be freed from her enemies and have no trouble. Rebecca sighed and thought to herself that all she too had wanted was to be free of her enemies and have no trouble. But now her mother's foolishness had brought them hostility on all sides.

'Prudence Hart,' Rebecca hissed. 'I wished her ill. I wished her lame on the right side.'

And then it all came into her head, those nights at Elizabeth Clarke's house – that hovel that reeked of cats' piss and dogs' dung and those mad old women with their books of hellish woodcuts they had bought from the pedlar, showing headless bears and witches who walked on water. And the talk of the gentry who turned the old from their doors, and the shopkeepers who would not give a single grant of credit for the smallest piece of cheese. It made her shiver and shake with tears and the words died on her lips. The magistrates looked at the thin girl and whispered of mercy among themselves.

She was back, back in the dark with those mad old women, but now they were in the dungeons of ruined Colchester Castle, fettered hand and foot and lying on the floor in their own filth. She was past gagging but the fear was with her when the jailer shook her arms and took her through the vast, studded oak door to a side room lit by a single candle.

Even in the shadows she knew who sat at the table – Matthew Hopkins. In the broad light of day in the streets of Manningtree she had found him vaguely comic, for his tall hat and bucket boots and clanking spurs had made his small stature ridiculous but now, in this foul place, his pale face and intense dark eyes made him menacing. He was being polite, inviting her to sit and giving her water from a tin can, but it was obvious he was here for a reason.

'Tell me more. We know you want to. It would be to your advantage if you could tell us of those meetings …' Hopkins put a vast key down on the table between them. It was only a suggestion, but the thought of freedom made her heart beat faster.

'Tell me, how did you first become a witch?'

Images flooded into her head and at last she spoke. 'About a year ago, I was walking towards Manningtree …'

'With whom?'

'With my mother, and she told me she was going to Elizabeth Clarke's house. An hour before sunset she took my hand and said, "Whatever you see tonight must be kept secret", so we went to the house and there they sat – Ann Leech and her daughter Helen, Elizabeth Gooding and Elizabeth Clarke – and then it began, the muttering and the mumbling and, in the midst of all the calls for the familiars, in came those creatures. I don't need to tell you more for you have seen them for yourself, good sir. That night there were three dogs and two cats and they jumped into Elizabeth's lap and kissed her and they kissed everybody in the room except me. Then the women asked my mother if I was acquainted with the business and she said, "Yes and my girl knows better than to reveal anything that she sees or hears this night", but they did not leave it at that. Oh the things they said! They said if I was to tell I would endure more torments on earth than could be in hell and I told them I would keep their secret even if the rope was around my neck and I was ready to be hanged.' She put her trembling hands around her neck and looked him straight in the eye.

Something about her glance made him gasp. 'I promise you shall not hang. Only tell me what contract you made with the Devil?'

'As I was going to bed, the Devil came to me and said he would marry me. I was terrified yet I could not deny him. He kissed me but he was cold as clay, yet he kept me in his power for he took me so gently by the hand and led me to my bedchamber, and promised to be my loving husband till death and to avenge all my enemies. I promised to be his obedient servant till death and to deny God and Christ Jesus. And not long after that she lost her child. Prudence Hart, I mean, she miscarried. It is a dreadful thing to have taken Satan for your

God, Master Hopkins. I did not understand what I had done …
Is there no hope for me?'

'You are young and this was your mother's doing. We will take
you back to Manningtree where you can speak again to good
Rector Ede.' He ordered water and soap and promised that she
may yet be washed in the blood of Jesus.

The captain took her name and she bowed her head so no
one could recognise her. She wanted to hide behind her
new linen bonnet. She was bound now for the New World. She
had convinced them. She was free, but at night the nightmare
of the hanging bodies was still there. She would never be free of
her betrayal.

~ The Disappearing Witch ~

The line between wise woman and witch was never clear, even
to the witchfinders themselves. People in Colchester thought
they knew which one Betty Potter was. She was a witch, and
Matthew Hopkins, Witchfinder General, should be told.
Yet Betty had her supporters. A merchant, whose daughter she had
cured of a fever, was determined to help her. He felt guilty that
the small bag of coins with which he had rewarded her might have
aroused her neighbours' jealousy. He must find her somewhere safe
to live.

He did his best. He found her a cottage in a dip on the road out
of Boxted village, which even to this day they call Betty Potter's Dip.
Sadly, it brought misfortune. She would wait patiently by the dip
for heavy wagons coming down the road, and beg supplies of the

carters, but they invariably refused the wild-looking, tall, skinny woman who muttered under her breath. They were nervous of her. Old women muttering to themselves meant no good. Muttering was more than likely a curse, or so they thought. The Devil's curse was everywhere in this wicked world.

The lord at Rivers Hall thought he knew what had happened well enough when one of his carters returned from the mill, gabbling and shaking like a leaf.

'Are you bewitched, fellow?'

'Betty Potter has me in her power, my lord, and, foul old crone that she is, she will not lift the spell until I give her a sack of wheat.'

The lord's son had been listening at the door. He did not wait for his father's reply. He whistled for his horse and rode out to the nearby farms to collect a party to 'take' this cursed witch. Aye, they took her. They took her and they hanged pathetic Betty Potter from a tree in the hay meadow.

Oh! Hopkins came quickly enough when he heard. He was angry that he would have a victim missing from his great show trial at Chelmsford. He rode down the road in the blue of dusk and saw the outline of a woman's body suspended from the tree. Then suddenly she seemed to slide to the ground; she landed on her feet and ran off across the field as lithe as a greyhound, leaving only the dent of naked feet in the dew-stained grass. He saw that she had left her woollen skirt and linen blouse on the ground behind her.

He shouted, but she was gone into the approaching night. Yet if you should want a glimpse of her, you need only stand under that old oak which served as a gallows, on 21 October at midnight, and I promise you will see her again. It makes folk so nervous that even now many a road accident is reported at Betty Potter's Dip.

~ THE SEA-WITCH ~

The great witch hunt came to an end in the seventeenth century. A Suffolk vicar ranted his horror at how tragic it was that deformed old women with no one to protect them had become victims of the most terrible stories. For a while it seemed that this foolishness had stopped, but in Leigh-on-Sea in 1852 a bizarre story surfaced, centred round an old woman called Sarah Moore. Poor Sarah looked like witches are supposed to have looked throughout time, with a hare lip, a hooked nose, a bent back and a sharp tongue, but the stories about her were stranger than anything in the brother Grimms' tales.

It was said that Sarah had the ability to flash sparks from her eyes. Two children, in fact, were found to have been burnt in her house. What actually happened? Well, it was a blustery day and a group of children saw Sarah Moore leave her house. She told the children to play in their own yard, but they did not. They could tell by the way her door was banging in the wind that it was unlocked.

Once she was out of sight, they could not resist going into the house. They wanted so much to see what instruments of magic might be hidden there. To their delight, they saw a copper bubbling away, a half-finished meal and a candle on the table, and on the shelf by the stairs a lamp and several dirty bottles. It was the bottles that intrigued the children most. Eighteen-year-old Lizzie was meant to be in charge. She was known to not be very bright and suffered badly from chilblains, so they thought they might find a cure for her ailment. Her sister Janie was ten, Tommy was almost twelve and baby Em was just four.

It wasn't easy seeing things in the half light coming from the one dirty window. Lizzie took a candle to examine the bottles more thoroughly, while Tommy and Janie lifted the lid of the copper. Lizzie had just lifted the candle towards the shelf when they heard the sound of shuffling feet and the door latch clicking.

They all knew who that was and, sure enough, the witch stood in the doorway muttering curses. The children all ran to the far side of the room. A bottle fell over, spilling its contents over Lizzie and Em, and, most terrifying of all, the girl and the toddler burst into flames. Mother Moore ran towards them with a sack to try to put the flames out but they were too frightened of her and ran out of the house towards the creek. Their screams brought out the neighbours, who were horrified to find that the wind made matters worse.

A doctor and an undertaker had to be summoned. They got some sense out of Tommy. He said it was a bottle of paraffin that had fallen, sending the candle flying, and when Mother Moore had come in the wind had made the flames blaze. Janie wasn't having this. 'No, she did it! The sea-witch. She came in the door and sparks flashed from her eyes and they burst into flames. I saw her do it.'

The doctor tried to convince the child that it was the reflection of the flames in her eyes that had made it seem as if Mother Moore's eyes blazed.

'No, I was there. I seen it. She did. She did. And she tried to catch them in a sack.'

This time Tommy agreed. 'Yes, she did. She rushed at 'em with a sack and she tried to ketch 'em.'

For the rest of her life, Janie believed her sisters had died because a sea-witch's eyes had blazed out fire.

The story of Sarah's own death was even more alarming. It seemed she had the ability to foretell the future, which she did by filling a scatter pan with seawater and carefully scattering Thames sand into it. The water would cloud over and she would see visions of the future; she had even been able to forecast storms.

A new skipper came to the town who knew nothing of her special abilities. He walked straight past her when she shouted, 'Buy a wind from me.' Most of the Leigh men would have tossed her a coin to protect them from storms at sea, but not him. His crew set off from harbour only to find the sky turning black, the wind dropping and the sails listless. The crew were apprehensive and one man shouted, 'It's the witch, it's the witch.'

Thunder crashed, lightning streaked across the sky and the smack keeled over on its side. The skipper was beside himself with anger. 'I'll kill that perishing witch!' he screamed and hacked at the tangled rigging three times with an axe. The falling rigging was in danger of dragging them all under. Fortunately, by the third blow the storm stopped, the sun came out and a breeze sprang up. The men said nothing until they neared the harbour and there they saw something which really shook them. There lay the dead body of Sarah Moore, three bloody gashes on her head. Killed by a mightier magic than her own, according to the folk of Leigh!

~ STRANGE EVENTS AT CANEWDON ~

It always seems a little unjust that the pretty little church at Canewdon has so many superstitions associated with it. It surely must be because of its isolated position. One of the most persistent is that, as long as the church stands, there will always be six witches in Canewdon. If a stone falls from the tower, a witch will die. Charlotte Mason, in 1928, said there were three witches dressed in silk and three dressed in cotton, showing their social rank. An old man living in Rayleigh had told her that one was the wife of the parson and another was the wife of a butcher.

Historical documents show that there were indeed Canewdon women accused of witchcraft, but the best-known story is the tale of the witch who stole a bell from Latchingdon Church and then tried to bring it back in a washtub using feathers as oars. A waterman saw her but she bewitched him with the odd warning: 'You will speak of it when you think of it.' Sure enough, he did remember it, years later, when he heard the bells toll for the funeral of the witch. He was shocked to find the memory coming back to him after all those years. It had faded away for so long but now it stood out as sharply as one of the cheap woodcuts that the pedlars used to sell.

A variation on this story is set in the graveyard. White vapour apparently appeared above the west gate in a shadowy cloud and took on the shape of a woman. This woman paralysed all who saw her with the power of her eyes. Anyone who met her out in the fields found themselves lifted up by a mysterious force and thrown over the hedgerow. Pleased with her work, she decided to ride on a hurdle down to the river, and crossed to the other side in a washtub using feathers as oars.

The most sinister figure in Canewdon was old George. Old George Pickingell, along with Cunning Murrell, boasted of being one of the 'cunning men' of Essex. Unlike Murrell, he was not liked. He was a farm labourer who it was said could clear a field at harvest time in half an hour with the help of his 'imps'. Local farmers were wary of him for he'd demand money or beer from them, threatening that if they did not agree he would blight their crops or put a hex on their farm machinery. Boys raced to get water for him from the village pump out of fear. He would strike at the hedgerow with his stick, sending game animals racing out that could be caught easily for food.

People who looked in his cottage would sometimes see his ornaments rise and fall in a merry dance. Many went to him to have their ailments cured. He lived to a grand old age and, as he lay dying, he promised he would show his powers. Sure enough he did. As the hearse drew up at the church, the horse walked away from the shafts and galloped down the road. There were some who said he had even stronger powers and that he had organised nine covens, but I will say no more.

Maybe, as in one superstition, you need to dance three times counter-clockwise round the church tower in order to go back into the past and find out the truth.

~ The Poacher and the Mawkin ~

(Inspired by H. Cranmer-Byng's story 'The Magic Mawkin')

There was a story they used to tell in the village about the poacher and the mawkin – which children loved, but it's not told very often these days. It could be that today's children are unfamiliar with poachers, let alone mawkins! A mawkin is an old Essex word for a scarecrow. Yes, there was a proper rustic dialect once, which sadly has been drowned by 'Estuary English'.

To get back to our story, there was once a poacher whose name was Samuel Peacock, although he was more commonly known as 'Owd Knowall'. This June evening, his missus had a longing for rabbit pie. There was no shortage of rabbits, but there were problems hunting them down. Up at the manor, they now had an eager new gamekeeper with sharp eyes, who was not going to be easy to fool.

If you went down by the river, you had to pass a cottage owned by the widow woman, who many thought was a witch.

Most people might be nervous of her, but Owd Knowall was not so easily frightened. He just thought the stories about her were children's efforts to scare each other. 'I ain't afeard o' she,' he murmured to himself. So he set out for the river with his snares in his pocket and his sturdy walking stick in his hand.

It was a long overgrown path to the river. Dusk was falling and he could just about make out the outline of the witch's cottage against a buttery sky. It had the strangest crooked chimney and an unkempt thatched roof which came down low over the house like hairy eyebrows. The windows glinted menacingly red in the fading rays of the sun. Sam held his breath for a moment. He wondered if the witch herself might rise into the sky with her familiar jackdaw on the side of her broomstick. The idea gave him the creeps.

Not long after that he became convinced that he had caught a glimpse of her standing in a field of young barley close to the lane. It was a little perplexing. She seemed not to be moving for some time and Sam was losing patience. He needed to see more clearly, so he walked up to higher ground. From there he could see young rabbits gambolling and playing happily around the feet of the motionless figure. Then he realised what he was seeing. The motionless figure was a mawkin set up to scare the birds. 'Cunning old girl,' he chuckled to himself, sure it was the widow's work.

Confidently he set to work, putting snares in the holes and runs in the hedgerow. Then he got another fright. It was an uncanny kind of chuckle coming from the direction of the stile. Gathering up his courage, he moved a little closer and then saw it was a jackdaw staring at him with its head on one side. Surely its mistress would follow soon. The bird rose in the air and started flying towards him. Sam raised his stick but suddenly a woman stood laughing in front of him. The bird flew down and perched itself on her stick. She certainly was no beauty – short and fat, she had a hooked nose, bloodshot eyes and heavy wrinkles like an aged hound. She was so stocky that she looked almost like a man in woman's clothes, and her crooked stick towered above her.

'Ho! Muster Knowall. And what be you doing here? Why might ye be a coming to see me?'

His throat went dry. He tried hard to think of a reason why he might be coming to see her. A love potion? A cure for warts? A wax dummy of the hated gamekeeper? Nothing seemed totally convincing, but, in the end, he made an offer. He offered to be her 'looker', the person who would keep people away from her and keep vermin down.

She was impressed. A wind made the pivoted head of the mawkin nod. There was a chill in the air and he heard her say, 'No! That,' pointing to the mawkin, 'will run faster than you, I'll lay down my own hat, it will ketch anything I want.' Alarmed, he turned and went, not bothering to pick up his snares.

He waited until dawn to rescue his snares and found, to his delight, that he had picked up four young rabbits. He was about to lift up a fifth, when he heard a rustle by the stile and knew something was moving in the barley field. He looked over and saw the mawkin. He was convinced it had moved, but for the moment it was totally still. The widow must have moved it in the night. But suddenly, to Sam's horror, he was looking right in the mawkin's face. It was not a pretty sight. There was something about the tattered and stained dishcloth making the face, and burst holes making the eyes, that filled him full of dread. His stomach tightened with fear and he tried to crawl into the undergrowth but he could still see that mask-like face staring at him.

Then came the voice – the strange, strained voice of the mawkin. 'Hoo, Ho, Muster Knowall, d'ye gi'eme your coat, Muster Knowall. I'm acowld. I'm a c-cowld.' Gradually the voice was growing deeper and more threatening. The demand for a coat was now being backed by the threat of turning Sam into stone with the use of his crooked stick. Sam was paralysed by fear. The stick seemed to be getting closer and closer to him. 'I'll gi'e ye. I'll gi'e ye,' he squealed. Pulling off his coat desperately, Sam flung it over the fence with the rabbits still bulging from its pockets.

'Hoo, hoo and now gi'e me yer trousers me dear, fur me legs is cowld too.'

'Be danged ef I do.'

Sam had found his courage at last and ran and ran, determined to suffer no more humiliation. Early risers watched his desperate run in puzzlement.

Sam's wife never quite understood why she didn't get her rabbit pie that day. She could smell one cooking at the widow's house. She asked her husband to go and request a couple of slices in exchange for some ripe strawberries, but her husband was firm. 'We'll have no more doings with them cursed witches,' and indeed they did not!

Five

WOMEN IN LOVE

Sadly, when Daniel Defoe visited the Eastern Counties, he noticed that:

> It was very frequent to meet with men that had from five to six to fourteen or fifteen wives, nay, and some more ... The reason as a merry fellow told me was this: that, they being bred from the marshes themselves and seasoned to the place did pretty well, but they always went to the upland for a wife. That when they took the young lasses out of the wholesome, fresh air they were healthy but they presently changed complexion, got an ague or two, and seldom held it above half a year or a year at most.

Yet despite this, romance flourished in Essex. In December 1904 the composer Vaughan Williams went to tea at Ingrave Rectory and there he heard an illiterate farm labourer called Charles Potiphar sing 'Bushes and Briars'. It was the beginning of Vaughan Williams' collection of Essex folk songs. This song introduces the more romantic side of Essex. The lines in the song which say 'I cannot think the reason why young women love young men' seems to echo through all the stories which follow.

'The King of Colchester's Daughter' is a strictly traditional story with roots going far back into the past. Its initial appearance in Essex was most likely in a chapbook called

'The History of the Four Kings'. The kings all rule places beginning with 'C' – Canterbury, Colchester, Cornwall and Cumberland. The strange reference to the heads in the well in the Colchester story may have Celtic echoes, when severed heads had connections with wells. The head's rhyme makes an appearance in the 1595 play *The Old Wives' Tale*. It is curiously haunting.

'The Three Big Sillies' is told in many parts of the country and has at least half a dozen versions. It was known to be told in Essex in 1800. I have to confess that I embroidered the tale in my own personal way to provoke a laugh in a modern audience, which it nearly always gets.

Real events often inspire the most romantic stories. The story about Matilda Fitzwalter is based on a historic character, but her story was embellished by two writers in the seventeenth century, so Matilda the Fair became known as Maid Marian. I found her alabaster tomb in Little Dunmow Church to be very touching, especially as I only managed to track the church down after being misdirected by a twisted signpost.

Finding the family tomb of the runaway bride Frances Riche, in All Saints' Church, Maldon, was an even bigger struggle. It was Carl Merry who found me the story of a love potion given by Cunning Murrell.

Many of the lovely ladies' ghosts still haunt us. I have a strong suspicion that Lucy, in 'The Smell of Violets', may have inspired the image of Miss Havisham. Dickens was known to be visiting Canvey Island at the time of her sad death.

~ BUSHES AND BRIARS ~

Through bushes and through briars
I lately took my way
All for to hear the small birds sing
And the lambs to skip and play
All for to hear the small birds sing
And the lambs to skip and play.

I overheard my own true love,
Her voice it rang so clear,
Long time I have been waiting for
The coming of my dear.

I drew myself unto a tree,
A tree that did look green
Where the leaves shaded over us
We scarcely could be seen.

I sat myself down by my true love
Till she began to mourn,
I'm of this opinion
That my heart is not my own.

Sometimes I am uneasy
And troubled in my mind,
Sometimes I think I'll go to my love
And tell to him my mind.

And if I should go to my love
My love he will say nay,
If I show to him my boldness
He'll ne'er love me again.

I cannot think the reason
Young women love young men
For they are so false hearted
Young women to trepan.*

For they are so false hearted
Young women to trepan
So the green grass shall see me
For I can't love that man.

* to entrap or beguile

⚊ THE KING OF COLCHESTER'S DAUGHTER ⚊

Long before the days of King Arthur and his knights there was a king who had everything a monarch might want. No enemies invaded his kingdom of Colchester; his people lived in harmony with each other; the land around produced fine corn; and there were oysters and all kinds of fine food to eat. Above all he had a beautiful wife and a lovely daughter. Then tragedy came. On his daughter's fifteenth birthday, his wife died.

Now, you would have thought it was a sensible idea to marry for a second time, if only for the sake of the motherless child; but you should have seen his choice of a second wife! She may have been wealthy, but she was a hideous creature with her hooked nose and humped back. Even worse, she was foul-tempered. To add to the King's troubles, his new stepdaughter was the image of her mother both in looks and temperament. The pair of them were eaten alive with envy of the King's daughter, for she was all they were not. She carried herself with dignity and was sweet-natured with a sunny temper.

The palace became a place of slander, squabbles, spitting tongues and spite. The King's daughter was desperately unhappy. She felt that even her father had had his mind poisoned against her. Luckily, she met her father early one evening in the garden, where the air was heavy with the smell of lavender and roses. He was on his own. At last she felt she could speak openly to him. Her eyes filled with tears looking into that dearly loved face again.

'Father, I am afraid I cannot live with my stepmother and stepsister. Do you think you could give me a small allowance, so I could leave home and make my own way in the world?'

'I am sorry you feel this way, my dear, but perhaps it might be best if you were to go,' he replied. And then foolishly he sent her to the stepmother for her allowance. What was she given? Nothing but a canvas bag containing bread, hard cheese and a bottle of beer! She did not complain but thanked her and set out on the road.

After she had passed many groves, woods and valleys she came to a cave, in front of which sat an old man. Stroking his long beard, he asked her, 'Where are you going, my pretty one?'

'I am going to seek my fortune.'

'And what do you have in that canvas bag?'

'I have bread and cheese and beer. Would you like some?'

'Thank you. I would!' He drank and ate eagerly, but then it was his turn to do her a favour. He gave her a warning about a thorny hedge that she would encounter on her way. He put a hazel branch in her hand and told her to touch the hedge three times and say 'Pray hedge, let me come through', and the hedge would then open up. Even more mysteriously, she would come to a well and from out of this well three golden heads would appear to her and she must do what they told her.

Sure enough, after a while she came to the prickly hedge. She spoke the magic words and tapped the branches with her wand. The hedge opened into the clearing and there she saw the well. From out of the well came a golden head singing the strangest song.

> Wash me, comb me,
> Lay me down softly
> And lay me on a bank to dry
> So that I look pretty
> When somebody passes me by

She had a silver comb in her pocket and, as gently as she could, she combed the golden head and laid it on a mossy bank where primroses, violets and celandines grew.

No sooner was it on the ground when up came a second and a third head, each time singing the strange song; each time she did as they asked. Then, when they requested to be returned to the well, she obeyed. In the depths of the well they whispered. They made promises to return this girl's kindness.

'She is beautiful already, but I will add the gift of charm,' the first head said.

'I will make her breath and body so fragrant, it will exceed the perfume of flowers,' added the second head.

The third head gave an even greater gift. 'She shall marry the best of princes.'

Amazingly, that very night, as the girl reached the outskirts of the great oak wood, a prince emerged from the shadows with his huntsmen and hounds. One glance at the princess in the rosy light of the setting sun and he was smitten, so smitten that he took her to his own castle for safety. There she was treated with the greatest of respect and given fine clothes and jewels. Love touched them so quickly that a wedding was not long in coming.

Only after the wedding did she tell him that she was the King of Colchester's daughter. 'The King of Colchester's daughter! How dearly you must be missed! We must arrange a visit as quickly as we can.' The prince was determined to make a great impression and they went to Colchester in a golden chariot lined with purple velvet, with blood-red garnets embedded in its sides.

You can imagine what happened when they got to Colchester. The King was delighted to see the young couple, but the stepmother and stepsister were frantic with jealousy and could not bear to watch the dancing and feasting that ensued.

'Let me go out on that road and let's see what good fortune comes my way,' the stepsister begged her mother. Her mother, of course, agreed, but her daughter was given fine travelling clothes to wear and a hamper that contained sweetmeats, roast boar sandwiches and a large bottle of the finest dry Spanish sherry. She took the same road and came to the same cave where the old man with the long beard sat.

'Where are you going in such a hurry, young woman?' he asked.

'That's none of your business.'

'And I suppose it's none of my business to know what you have in your hamper.'

'True, for I would share none of it unless I knew it would choke you.'

The old man muttered curses on her head as she left and, of course, he did not warn her about the hedge and the well.

At the hedge she thought she saw a gap, but she was wrong. As she pushed her way through, the thorns tore at her hands and arms so she bled profusely. Desperately she looked around to find water to wash away the blood – and then she saw the well. When she got close to it she saw the first golden head, and it was singing that strange song.

> Wash me, comb me,
> Lay me down softly
> And lay me on a bank to dry
> So that I look pretty
> When somebody passes me by

But what a reaction! The stepsister took the bottle of sherry and knocked the head down the well, shouting, 'Take that for your washing!' This she did to the second and the third head as they rose from the well. They sank back in the darkness whimpering with pain and whispered among themselves what they must do.

'I'll give her sores all over her face,' the first head vowed.

'I'll make her smell like a pig in shit,' said the second head.

The third head said, 'And her husband shall be no better than a poor cobbler.'

Oblivious to the changes that were happening to her, the girl set off for the nearest market town. No sooner had she arrived at the market than people started to move away from her, for they could not stand to see her ugly face or be near that stink. Only a cobbler came up to her, for in his pocket he had a box of ointment that could cure sores and a bottle of spirits that could freshen mouth and body. He had obtained these as a reward for mending the shoes of a hermit. He offered them to her in return for becoming her husband. To his delight, she said, 'With all my heart' – although at first she had been full of how she was the King of Colchester's daughter. In fact, she was so relieved that her sores and bad breath were gone that she was happy enough to snuggle into his arms.

Not long after their wedding, the cobbler and his wife went to Colchester. The girl's mother was horrified to see her daughter fallen so low and married to a cobbler of all people, and the foolish woman took her own life. Her husband inherited her wealth and, out of that fortune, he gave the cobbler £100 for him and his wife to start a new life in a remote village. The cobbler became a fine mender of shoes and his wife wove as fine a thread as is woven into this tale, for it is a story of love.

~ THE THREE BIG SILLIES ~

It was always said there was no prettier village in Essex than Finchingfield, with its thatched cottages and duck pond. In that village there was no couple more in love than Tom the ploughman and his sweetheart pretty Lizzie Simons. Yet Lizzie, her mother and father were having trouble fixing the wedding date. It was because they always liked to have something to worry about. It was their way. They were proper sillies about it. Take these examples. Her mother thought: 'Suppose at the wedding the girl trips over her wedding veil?' Her father thought: 'Suppose after the wedding, Tom finds out what a bad cook she is? Nothing like her mother!' Lizzie thought: 'Oh dear, what sort of mother shall I make? Children are so difficult.'

Tom would sigh, kiss Lizzie and pooh-pooh all their doubts. 'Everybody worries before a wedding,' he would say, having none of it. Then one day he completely lost his temper. 'If I could find three people as silly as you folks, surely you would let the wedding happen then?'

Lizzie's smile spread across her cheeks and her eyes twinkled. He guessed what the answer might be.

That very night Tom set out on the open road and stayed the night at the inn in the next village. Imagine his amazement when he walked by the village pond late that evening and saw all the villagers dragging rakes and brooms and pickaxes across the water.

'Why are you doing that?'

'The moon has fallen in the pond and we are trying to drag her up again,' replied one.

Tom smiled to himself. Here was foolishness indeed! Imagine not being able to recognise the moon's reflection. When he returned to the inn, the place was so full that he had to share a room with an old man. He noticed that before they went to sleep the old man hung his trousers by their braces from the knobs of the chest of drawers. Yet he seemed a sensible enough old fellow and very friendly.

In the morning, he watched in amazement as the old man ran across the room and tried to jump into his trousers where they hung. The old man tried over and over again but he still could not manage it.

'Why are you doing that?' Tom asked.

'Isn't that how everyone gets into their trousers? It takes the best part of an hour to get into mine in the morning and I get so hot. I swear trousers are the most awkward thing ever invented.'

Tom roared with laughter and showed the old man how he put his own trousers on. The old man was very grateful. Tom smiled and knew he had found fool number two.

The next day he set out on the road and found an old woman trying to push her cow up the chimney so it could get up on the roof.

'Why are you doing that?'

'The roof is the only place where the grass grows round here. If only the cow would go up the ladder onto the roof, then think how well fed she would be.'

'Then, my dear,' he said, 'why don't you go up the ladder and cut the grass off the roof and throw it down to the cow?'

The old lady would have none of that. She had it all sorted in her head. She pushed and shoved the poor old cow up the ladder, then tied string around its neck and passed the string down the chimney, fastening it to her own wrist as she went around doing her housework. I think you can guess what happened. The cow tumbled off the roof and got strangled by the string. The weight of the cow tied round the old lady's wrist dragged the old lady up the chimney until she was stuck halfway up and covered in soot. Tom was sorry at the sight but there was no denying that here was big silly number three.

When he got home and told Lizzie and her family about these three big sillies, all their misgivings faded and they agreed to a wedding the very next Saturday. There was no prettier bride in her little crinoline skirt than Lizzie, and she walked up the aisle blushing and proud as a bantam hen, with never a stumble.

From the very first day of their married life she cooked some fine meals – the creamiest porridge you have ever tasted, stews full of tender meat and delicious vegetables, and pies with pastry that melted in the mouth. She had been learning to cook from her mother all her life. And as for their children – what darlings they all were! Never a quarrel or a bad word.

Ah! Now at last you know what I have been doing – I have been telling you a fairy tale!

⚊ The Romantic History of ⚊
Matilda Fitzwalter

There are few who know that 'Maid Marian' is buried in the lovely Lady Chapel of Little Dunmow Church. There she lies in a splendid tomb, one of the most romantic ladies in English history. Some call her Matilda Fitzwalter. Some call her Maid Marian. Look down at her effigy of alabaster and it is possible to make out, in the soft white glow, a sweet face covered with a simple coif. Around the neck is a collar of pendants falling on a richly embroidered kerchief. Around the waist is a rich girdle, the arms are covered with split sleeves close to the wrist, and her fingers are loaded with rings. Obviously here is a lady of great wealth and beauty, so how did she come to meet with so sad a death?

The romantic career of Matilda Fitzwalter, as she was first called, began on her eighteenth birthday, when her father gave a tournament in her honour at one of his castles. It was planned to last for three days and everybody was pleased that Matilda was crowned the Queen of Beauty at the event. Unluckily for her, sitting by her side was the loathsome Prince John. From his face it was clear what manner of man he was. He had the look of a wolf and eyes that glittered with lust. Every time Matilda looked at him she shuddered at the thought of his lechery.

Then, on the fourth day, a new champion appeared. He came in burnished mail, carrying a shield bare of emblems and waving his sword with such effect that he outfought every challenger. As Matilda hung the victor's chain around his neck, she caught a glimpse of honest blue eyes and the fresh face of a man who lived in the outdoors. Her young heart fluttered with delight. She leant forward to whisper her praises, but he was gone to the forest before she could say a word.

During the months that followed it was politics that dominated the mind of Prince John. He became totally embroiled in all sorts of arguments with his barons. It seemed like a state of war existed. Prince John attacked the Fitzwalter castle and killed Matilda's father. Terrified, she sought refuge in the forest. Crashing through the bracken, she made her way deeper and deeper into the rustling leaves of the mighty trees. For a whole night and half a day she pressed on, until suddenly, from behind a gnarled oak, a tall man dressed in Lincoln green and carrying a longbow appeared before her. Immediately she knew who it was – it was the champion from her birthday joust! She could barely contain her joy. He was Robin Hood, the outlawed Earl of Huntingdon.

As time went on, Matilda found the simple life of the forest suited her well. She asked Robin's faithful followers to call her by the name Maid Marian. Surrounded by the strength of these loyal men, she learnt to trust again. A great love grew between her and Robin. It was inevitable that there should be a wedding and the green wood rang with the sounds of merriment.

The couple's joy increased when good King Richard returned; one of his first deeds was to restore Robin's estates and rank, and now Maid Marian had yet another title – she was the Countess of Huntingdon. Could life continue to be as agreeable as this? No! The villain John was still weaving his web of evil. His brother Richard, careless of his life, sickened with gangrene from a wound neglected on the battlefield and died. John was crowned king and people like the Earl of Huntingdon had no place in his court.

Once again the Earl and his lady were known as Robin Hood and Maid Marian, and they went back to the forest with their old followers. They were older now and life was harsher than it had ever been. So harsh that Robin died and Marian made her way back to Essex, where she found sanctuary with the nuns of Dunmow Priory.

Even there, she was not safe. King John knew of her whereabouts and sent Sir Robert de Medieve to present her with a fine pair of gloves. Sir Robert assumed it was a love token and had no idea that the gloves were impregnated with poison.

As Sir Robert rode away after presenting the gift, his mind was full of the lovely lady he had just met. Matilda was now of mature years, but there was still a glow about her that enchanted men. Sir Robert rode through the trees that surrounded the priory deep in thought. Then, as dusk fell, a premonition of something evil affected him deeply. Turning his horse around, he galloped back to where the light shone from the priory church. The priory seemed deserted but the church itself was ablaze with the light of many tapers and there was the sound of a funeral dirge. The ring of his armour could be heard as he walked into the church – and then he paused in horror. Lying in front of the altar, on a bier surrounded by flowers, was the dead body of the beautiful Matilda. The poison from the gloves had had its effect and eaten into her flesh. Robert flung himself on the bier, cursing himself for his foolishness and vowing never to be in the King's service again. It took the nuns many hours to persuade him to leave that place. In fact, he never returned to court. Sir Robert put aside his suit of mail and entered Dunmow Priory as an Augustinian monk, praying every day for forgiveness.

~ LOVE AT THE FERRY ~

It's a challenge to find the magnificent family Cammock memorial in All Saints' Church in Maldon. It certainly seems impressive in the photographs, yet when I visited the church I was totally mystified and could not see it anywhere. Even people I asked in the street outside did not know where it was. Back into the church I went and, standing in front of the altar,

I caught a glimpse of it beyond a partition. I will not tell you exactly how I found it, but will say that it is worth finding and the story associated with it is even more intriguing.

When you get close to the monument, you can see on the top level two women in black Tudor dresses and white ruffs kneeling before a bearded gentleman in a fur-lined robe. Beneath this odd trio are: on the left side four boys and five girls; on the right side two boys and eleven girls. This on its own might suggest why Captain Cammock deserved so fine a monument. Fathering twenty-two children seems a remarkable achievement!

So who were these people? Captain Thomas Cammock was a country gentleman who just cleared the rank of yeoman. On one side of him kneels his first wife, Ursula Wyrley of Didford, and below her are her nine children. On the other side of Captain Cammock is his second wife Frances Riche, daughter of Sir Robert, 2nd Earl Riche, and below her are her thirteen children. The story of the courtship of Thomas and his second wife Frances deserves to be retold at many a fireside, and Frances should be celebrated as one of Essex's feistiest ladies.

As in all real romances, Frances and Thomas were a pair of star-crossed lovers. Frances was the daughter of the Earl of Warwick, her sweetheart's high-ranking employer. He was scarcely likely to approve of a middle-aged widower with nine children marrying his lovely young daughter. The captain may have been a man with a swagger and plenty of charm, but fathers have never been taken in by charm alone. An Elizabethan father, in particular, would have looked for wealth and social status in a potential son-in-law. Thomas appeared to have neither.

Frances did not care. She was besotted with Thomas. Then, one happy day, an opportunity came for them to elope. Thomas was riding with the Riche retinue between Great Leighs and Rochford, on the back of a fine filly, when he could no longer control himself. He swooped his darling onto his horse behind him and off they galloped. To their horror, they heard the sound of galloping hooves behind them. Frances turned her head to see who it was. It was her father! She put her arms around Thomas' waist and whispered, 'My father's following us.'

Thomas turned and saw it was true and, laying his reins across the horse's neck, urged it to greater speed. 'Fambridge Ferry! Hurry! Hurry!' At least from there, he thought, they would be able to cross to Maldon.

On and on they galloped, until they reached the river Crouch. The day was turning grey and the storm clouds were gathering, but they could still make out that the ferry boat was on the furthest bank of the river.

'We could swim the river,' the infatuated girl said.

'It's too dangerous. The tides are too unreliable.'

'I don't care. I will live or die with you, my darling Thomas.'

With one accord the horse, the man and the girl all sank into the water. They swam as far as the middle of the river before they caught the sound of Frances' father's horses neighing behind them. Their own horse pricked up its ears and very nearly turned back, but the lovers were too strong and the horse continued to swim to the safety of the opposite bank, where they rode on to Maldon. There the accounts of the time said they were 'married and bedded'.

And how did the father react when he heard the full story? His followers waited for an explosion of anger, but instead the Earl smiled and said, 'Seeing that Francis has ventured her life for Thomas Cammock – God bless them.'

God bless them, so say I. What a shame that Thomas Cammock is only remembered in Maldon for giving the town its first water supply. Mind you, the old water pump on Cromwell Hill is easier to find than the Cammock monument.

~ The Heart of Thorns ~

(Story told by Carl Merry)

It was the last Saturday before Christmas, and in the church at Leigh-on-Sea the choir was rehearsing for the carol service the next day. The young people of the parish had also gathered to help decorate the church. Rosie thought it was she who had the best job, for she had been asked to work on the nativity scene. She placed the stable on a table, took the beautifully carved wooden figures from the box, and began to place them ever so carefully to create the scene of Christ's birth. Rosie gave all her attention to this task, arranging and rearranging the figures to create the best effect. She shifted the three candles which illuminated the scene until she was satisfied that it was perfect. It was only when she looked up expecting to receive praise from her friends that she realised she was alone in the church. The choir had long since gone home and the young men and women had also left.

So Rosie stood and pulled on her thick coat and began to walk up the aisle, only to stop halfway. For there, through the half-open church door, she saw her boyfriend Frank with another girl in his arms. He was kissing Elizabeth! Rosie sank into one of the pews and sobbed quietly to herself. Her heart was broken. She sat and cried for some time until she was sure that Frank and Elizabeth had left the church porch. She had heard their footsteps crunch on the crisp snow that had been falling throughout the evening. It was not until those footsteps faded into silence that Rosie left her seat and made her way down the hill towards her parents' house. When she reached the house she ran into the hallway and up the stairs to her bedroom with not a word to her parents. There she undressed, put on her nightdress, got into her bed and gave way to her sorrow once more.

She wept and wept until her pillow was so wet you could have wrung it out. But no sleep would come, so she rose from her bed and sat gazing out of her bedroom window. And as she sat looking towards the ruins of Hadleigh Castle, silhouetted against the moon she saw a figure walking. It was a small thin man, who had on a hard-glazed tile hat, the kind worn by sailors in the eighteenth century. He was carrying a small umbrella and, hanging from the handle of the umbrella, was a small wicker basket. She watched as he took an implement from the basket and bent down to dig.

'It's the cunning man,' she said to herself, 'digging up roots or plants for one of his potions. He could help me win back Frank.' So Rosie returned to her bed and sleep finally took hold of her body.

The next morning, when her parents called her for church, Rosie told them she was too ill to attend that day, but that they should go. 'The choir sang so sweetly last night it would be a shame for you to miss the carol service. You know how much you like it.'

As soon as her parents had left the house Rosie pulled on her clothes, wrapped a shawl around herself and set off down the narrow streets. Soon she found herself outside the cunning man's door. And there she stopped, plucking up the courage to knock. And knock she did. She heard footsteps coming down the hallway and, before very long, the door was opened by Cunning Murrell himself. He looked her up and down.

'It's Rosie, isn't it? How can I help you? Come inside.'

Rosie was taken into a room like none she had seen before. From every beam hung drying herbs and flowers. The scent of each plant the cunning man had picked filled the air and on every flat surface lay books. All sorts of books! Some were proper books with printed pages, all the way from London. But most were handwritten, in bold black ink and in a spidery, crabbed hand – books of spells, cures, potions and mysteries.

Rosie explained what had happened and asked for a spell or a potion to make Frank love her and not Elizabeth. Murrell nodded and asked her age, the date and time of her birth, and many other questions. Frank and Elizabeth's birth dates and times were also noted, as well as details of their lives. He wrote the information down in one of his books. Once he was satisfied that all questions had been answered, Murrell snapped his book shut and walked over to a cupboard. Taking down a small wooden box, he said, 'This will help you.' From the box he took a handful of thorns, thorns from the dog rose. 'Listen carefully and do as I say. At the next full moon you must go to the churchyard and sit under the moon. When it shines bright upon you, you must thrust these thorns into a heart made of red flannel. As you push in each thorn, spell out the name of your rival in love.' He gave her nine thorns, one for each letter of Elizabeth's name. Rosie thanked him, gave him a farthing and went on her way.

The next full moon was not until New Year's Eve. Rosie cut out a heart from red flannel as the cunning man had told her and waited for the night of the full moon. The evening of New Year's Eve came and Rosie sat looking out of her bedroom window, watching the young girls being taken up the hill to the church in a large cart. The young men were walking at the side of the cart smiling and talking to the girls … and Frank was talking to Elizabeth.

Rosie waited until darkness came. Only then did she climb the hill to the churchyard. She sat there with her back against a gravestone looking up at the sky, looking up for the full moon. But the night was cloudy and the moon shone no light on the graveyard or Rosie. She could hear the music, happiness and laughter of her friends and neighbours as they danced in the church hall. How long she sat it would be hard to tell. Just as she was thinking of returning home, however, the clouds parted and the moon shone down big and bright. Without a pause, Rosie took the thorns and the red flannel heart from her bag. She laid the heart on the ground before her and began to thrust in the thorns. With each thorn she called the letters of Elizabeth's name.

'E', a thorn, 'L', a thorn, 'I', a thorn … on she went until the final thorn was thrust hard into the red flannel heart. As she called out the last letter, there was a great explosion of noise which so frightened Rosie that she fainted straightaway. The next thing she knew, strong hands were lifting her from the cold ground and, when she opened her eyes, she was gazing into the eyes of her beloved Frank.

'Rosie, Rosie, I thought I'd lost you. When we came out of the dance, there you were laid out like the dead. Head against a gravestone and as still as death. It gave me such a fright.' Frank held her close and carried her from the churchyard down the hill towards her home. All the time Rosie was looking into his eyes and she saw behind the eyes his love for her – deep and true, unwavering love.

Halfway down the hill, a movement distracted her gaze and she looked over Frank's shoulder. Emerging from a side street was a man, a small thin man who had on a hard-glazed tile hat, the kind worn by sailors in the eighteenth century. He was carrying a small umbrella and, hanging from the handle of the umbrella, was a small wicker basket. Their eyes met and Cunning Murrell nodded. Frank and Rosie were married the following year.

~ THE SMELL OF VIOLETS ~

Everything in the Lobster Pot public house that day either rattled or creaked or banged. A chilly wind had come out of the sea and driven the rain against the ill-fitting windows of the inn. The fitful fire, the unwashed floor and a tin plate of grisly mutton were clear signs that the landlady was out for the day and Lucy, her sixteen-year-old daughter, had been left in charge. Lucy was in a foul mood. Slop, slop, she went as she slapped her dishcloth against the beer-stained table. Her mob-cap flopped down over her face and she looked down in disgust at her sacking apron. She began to raucously sing a song about the faithlessness of men. She had assumed she was alone, but then suddenly over the top of the settle appeared a pair of laughing blue eyes. 'What angel wakes me?' he laughed. It was Jack the sailor. He had obviously fallen asleep on the settle the night before.

'Don't mock me!'

'I don't. Come here, my pretty maid.' Before she knew it, he had kissed her once, twice, three times. And very sweet those kisses were too.

And that was how it all began – the romance of Jack and Lucy. The other serving wenches warned her about the wicked ways of those who wore the 'tarry trousers'. Her mother kept insisting that she would be better suited marrying the local tailor whose respectability was never doubted and who could be guaranteed to earn a decent living.

Strangely enough, however, Jack behaved towards Lucy with the utmost respect, and as he prepared to leave for sea he vowed he would be home in the spring and they would be married at St Katherine's Church. It was what she had always dreamt of. He gave her a ring which she hung on a ribbon around her neck, for she never told her mother about her engagement.

For the entire winter that Jack was away, she went through the motions of being polite to the tailor, although even he could sense there was something a little reserved about her manner. 'She's not interested, I tell you, Mistress Godfrey,' he would say to Lucy's mother, and Lucy would run off to her room to avoid her mother's nagging. It was there that she kept her secret. Night after night she burnt out candles as she sewed the lovely wedding dress that she planned to wear at her wedding to Jack.

At last a little sunshine began to appear after the ice and snow. Nowhere is as cold as Canvey Island in winter. Lucy smiled when she saw the violets come out in the hedgerows. It would not be long now before Jack was home. But then her world fell to pieces one day. A man entered the inn with a newspaper article describing a terrible storm in Nova Scotia, and she saw the name of her beloved among the men that had been lost. She howled so piteously that even her mother got to hear the full story and would not say a bad word against Jack. She hugged her daughter tightly, trying desperately to comfort her.

For the next month Lucy went about her duties mechanically, barely speaking a word to anyone. She was growing thinner and thinner until gradually she pined away. They buried her in St Katherine's graveyard in that lovely wedding dress she had worked so hard to make. They say that in the spring of every year on Canvey Island her ghost appears in her wedding gown, wailing down the Bride's Walk, and you know when she comes for that is when you smell the violets.

~ JACKY ROBINSON ~

(Traditional / © Adrian May & Potiphar's Apprentices, 2009)

The perils and dangers of the voyage are past
And the ship at Portsmouth has arrived at last
The sails all furled and the anchors cast
And the happiest of the crew is Jacky Robinson

He met with a man and he says 'I say
Perhaps you know one Polly Gray
She's somewhere hereabouts,' the man replied
'I do not indeed' to Jacky Robinson.

In a public house they both sat down
And talked of Admirals of high renown
And drunk as much grog as came to half a crown
This here strange man and Jacky Robinson

When Jack called out the reckoning to pay
The landlady came in, in fine array
'Well! Damn my eyes, why here is Polly Gray
Who'd have thought of meeting her here,' says Jacky Robinson

Says the lady, says she, 'I've changed my state'
'Why, you don't mean,' says Jacky, 'that you've got a mate?
You know you promised'; says she 'I could not wait
For no tidings could I gain of Jacky Robinson

And somebody, one day, came up and said
That somebody else had somewhere read

In some newspaper as how you might be dead.'
'I've not been dead at all' says Jacky Robinson

'But to fret and to stew about it's all in vain
I'll ship out to Holland, France and Spain
No matter where but I'll ne'er come here again'
And he was off before you could say Jacky Robinson

Six

THINGS THAT GO
BUMP IN THE NIGHT

When I first moved to Essex, I noticed that when I travelled at night away from the towns into the open countryside, it seemed as if I was being plunged into a very deep blackness, where all sorts of alarming things could happen. Indeed, medieval Essex had countless stories concerning the dark and the Devil, of which the most famous is the very strange story of the building of Barn Hall. The Devil even turns up to help with the harvest on Mersea Island.

The attractive porch to St Leonard's on the Hythe at Colchester has long sheltered five ghosts. White Ladies have appeared at Hadleigh Castle and I have to confess that in the story of 'Lament for a White Lady' I have taken liberties with a reference Baring-Gould made to the sighting of a White Lady in East Mersea.

An isolated, moated farm on the outskirts of Clavering was the perfect setting for murder and the melodramatic events that resulted in the death of Camille Cecile Holland at the hands of Samuel Dougal, the unlikely charmer. The haunting Tollesbury

Marshes are a fine place for the demon dog Black Shuck to make an appearance, and then there is the sad business of the ostler stuck up the chimney of a fine inn.

Fascination with the supernatural persists even today, with paranormal investigations becoming more and more popular. I feel uncomfortable with such activities and have only told ghost stories that have become well established over a long period of time.

– The Legend of Barn Hall –

This story comes from the depths of rural Essex, one of the most haunting landscapes in England. It is a tale that lingers long in the imagination. This is the remarkable legend of the building of Barn Hall in the parish of Tolleshunt Knights. It was first told by a character known as the hermit of Salcott. I know no more of the hermit, but it gives the tale credence!

A rich man had decided to build himself a fine home in the area known as the Devil's Wood. He had bought the best timber and hired the best workman he could afford to erect the building. It was a foolish move. In this very place it was rumoured that his Satanic Majesty and his followers held their wildest revels.

The Devil was angry that anyone should venture into his lands. He watched in disgust as the carpenters worked so hard on the new building. He waited until it was night before he decided to unleash what mischief he could. But to his amazement, the Devil realised someone was still on the site after dark. He called out, 'Who is there?'

The watchman replied, 'God and myself and my three spey bitches.'

The Devil felt uncomfortable at the mention of God and turned angrily into the darkness with a flick of his forked tail.

He came again the next night. 'Who is there?' he demanded.

Again he got the answer, 'God and myself and my three spey bitches.' So again the Devil vanished into the darkness.

The next night the watchman was growing tired, so when he was questioned by the Devil, he gave the answer, 'Myself and my three spey bitches and God.' Oh silly man! How could he be so foolish as to put his own name before that of the Almighty! The Devil had him in his power now. The Devil dug in his claws and removed the heart of the poor watchman, shrieking, 'I will have your soul wherever you are buried. Whether it be church or churchyard, field or road!'

Yet, thankfully, the watchman was buried inside the wall of the local church, a place not mentioned by the Devil. The Evil One had been cheated, yet in another sense Satan got his own way, for he had picked up the beam of the half-built house and tossed it high, shouting, 'Where this beam shall fall, there shall ye build Barn Hall.'

And so it was that Barn Hall was built some distance from the Devil's Wood. The beam, it seems, still remains in the cellar of the farm with the claw marks the Devil made. No one can touch it without hurting themselves. So, like all devilish things, it's best left alone.

The story has been so often told that there are several variations as to the fate of the hapless watchman. One interesting ending is that the Devil turned the man to stone and he was laid in the church, which had the strange nickname of the Bushes (possibly called this because the church is so far down a dirt track, among trees). It was thought that the man may have been buried in the wall of the church itself. Those who saw the effigy noticed that it had a gash in its stone side. The stone watchman wore a visor, was legless and held his heart in his hands!

I cannot untangle the story for myself. The church that was known as the Bushes is now so deep in the woods and so completely boarded up that no one can explore it. Its desolation is complete. I shuddered at its eeriness and went no closer.

~ The Thirteenth Reaper ~

Like so many of Essex's supernatural stories, this tale became known through one of James Wentworth Day's cronies. His name was Ted Allen and he lived on Mersea Island in a house called Hopping Tom's Piece by a pond called the Devil's Drink Bowl. Apparently he earned his living as a combination of gamekeeper, marsh-looker, cattleman, shepherd, adder catcher, bull tamer and 'general pirate'. This is his story of the thirteenth reaper.

It was the hay harvest and twelve men, known to the master of the hall, turned up to mow with their scythes – when a thirteenth man, a stranger, slipped in among them. He seemed to have a more splendid scythe than anyone else and went on mowing long after the other men had stopped. In fact, he went on mowing long into the night when the moon had come out. This made the other men uneasy and they slipped iron bars into the field where the stranger was working. Amazingly, the stranger went on cutting through the iron as though it was a slice of cheese.

'It's as if he were the Devil himself,' voices muttered.

When the stranger went to be paid by the squire up at the hall, the squire could not take his eyes off the man's feet. They were not feet at all, but cloven hooves! The squire rose to his feet, screaming, 'I won't pay you. I know who you are. Some may call you old Hopping Tom, but I know you are the Devil!'

There was no answer for a moment. Then a flicker of flame, a hideous shriek and the stranger ran outside, clutching his drinking bowl. With one almighty heave, he threw it into the centre of the field. The field flooded and the crops drowned. To this day the pond is known as the Devil's Drink Bowl.

~ THE ROBBERS AND THE BAKER ~

There is a redundant church on the hill of the Hythe at Colchester; it is still a very attractive Gothic building, with fine stained-glass windows and carvings, and an attractive porch with two storeys. Yet from the windows of the porch room, five ghosts look out at the busy traffic that passes below them and make their judgements on the modern world.

Four of the ghosts were once robbers who were caught stealing church plate. They were punished by being shut up in the porch room and left to starve. A baker passing by one night caught a glimpse of their sad white faces pressed against the window and tossed loaves of bread up to them. Sadly he was caught too, shut up with the robbers and left to starve to death. They say that five ghosts look out now in that quiet way of theirs. I wonder what they think as they see the modern people of Colchester bustle about their business. Has the world got any kinder since their day?

~ WRY NECK SAL ~

You find them all over the place – White Ladies who haunt castle ruins, appear at dawn, and then vanish after promising to reveal a secret. The White Lady that young Sal met at Hadleigh Castle was especially alarming.

The castle itself had been steadily decaying since the sixteenth century. The salty air, the unstable ground it was built on, and the greed of Lord Robert Riche meant that the castle was deteriorating into ruins. The undergrowth was creeping everywhere. To the romantic eye of the eighteenth century, these ruins had a special aura, so special that it inspired one of Constable's most dramatic paintings.

Sal, a milkmaid from a local farm, had to pass the castle on the way to the field where the cows were. It meant she had to be up very early, as milkmaids must. This spring day, a pale dawn was only just breaking. Sal had taken a shortcut near the castle when she saw, sliding from behind a bush, a lady in white. She was tall and thin and wore a curious robe of white knotted wool which trailed behind her over dew-soaked grass.

As the lady got nearer to her, Sal felt a cold breath on her cheek. It was still not possible to see the lady's face clearly. A white lace veil was pulled down too hard over her head. She could just catch the glitter of black eyes. Then Sal heard a whisper: 'Meet me here at midnight tonight. Then shall I tell you the mysteries of this place.' A shroud of sea mist came down over her and the lady vanished.

All day long the girl wondered what the 'mysteries' could be. She rather liked the idea of it being a tryst between the lady and her secret lover at the castle. The girl imagined a splendid fellow in shining armour with strong arms and laughing eyes. She imagined how wonderful it would be to be swept into the arms of such a fine man.

There was another possibility. Maybe the lady had buried treasure there? Could there be chests full of coins and plate hidden in all that trailing ivy? How wonderful if she could find such treasure to share with her family!

The thoughts went round and round in her head. By the time, however, that she had eaten her simple supper of bread and cold mutton, Sal began to feel apprehensive. Reality had got a grip of her. She had no desire to leave her family's cottage and venture into the dark. There was a steady downpour of drizzle. What would be the point of fighting her way in the wet to the cold stone ruins? The only thing she was likely to find there was a hungry ferret or sharp-toothed rat. White Lady indeed! It was more likely to be one of the smuggling boys playing a trick on her. She tossed and she turned, but by midnight she had sunk deep into the depths of her featherbed, which she shared with her sisters, and was fast asleep.

By morning everything seemed more promising and she set out cheerfully to milk the cows. She passed through the castle grounds again, and to her amazement the White Lady was waiting for her in the place where they had met the previous day.

'You didn't come. How dare you disobey me!' The ghost lifted her hand and gave Sal a cuff on the neck. It was amazing how strong she was. She almost dislocated the girl's neck. If you had seen Sal in the street after that, you would have recognised her easily as the one known as 'wry neck Sal'.

Even today children hurry away, bundling themselves up in their hoods when a white mist comes over Hadleigh Castle. They are terrified that the White Lady may come again and they sigh to think of the poor, hurt milkmaid all those centuries ago. They certainly go nowhere near the castle at midnight. Would you?

~ Lament for a White Lady ~

It was the summer of 1648 and for days it had done nothing but rain, rain and rain. The farmers of East Mersea were glad enough to sit in the Dog & Pheasant with their ale and grumble. There is no worse-tempered person than a farmer expecting a poor harvest. The harvest was all they cared about. The King might be in prison and Parliament at war with the nation but it meant nothing to the folk on the island. That was London business. Then in came young Tom, his face white and his red hair standing on end.

'Come, my masters, they're smashing the windows in our church.'

'Who?'

'The Parliament men.'

'What do they want with us?'

Barnaby, the oyster fisherman who had been everywhere and knew everything, spoke up. 'Haven't you heard? The Lord Goring has marched himself and his men into Colchester demanding men to rescue the King from jail.'

'Won't have much joy there. I hear they don't like the King in Colchester.'

'Ah! But the King's men have the power now in town. Old Sir Thomas Fairfax is sitting powerless at the gates.'

Fairfax's name was not known by many men on the island but they had no liking for the idea of soldiers being in East Mersea. This story of Tom's sounded alarming and, forming a little troop of their own, they marched off for the church, grabbing an odd pitchfork or rake on their way for reassurance.

They crept up to the church door slowly and immediately saw the broken windows, but amazingly there was no sound. All was silent! Gingerly they opened the door and there was nobody there.

The soldiers had gone but had left plenty of evidence of their presence. Not only were the windows open to the sky but the beautiful rood screen lay in splinters on the floor. Their mouths fell open. Why would anybody do such a thing in their lovely church, so isolated from all the hurly burly of politics?

An odd whimper came from the vestry and there they found the vicar hiding in a corner. He was shivering with fear. 'I didn't try to stop them. There were too many of them. Idolatry – that's what they said it was, those stupid, stupid Puritans. Said we weren't worshipping God in the right way.'

The men still did not understand. 'Where have they gone?'

'Gone to the fort.'

The men nodded. They had forgotten there was a small garrison of King's men still there. Parliament would need to remove them in order to prevent food getting through to Colchester. A mighty siege was being prepared.

'God help us!' muttered the vicar.

'Amen,' the men muttered.

Curiously, after a few days, the younger islanders became excited. Ann, the daughter of the innkeeper, was full of it. A spirited lass with flashing dark eyes and ripples of waving black hair, she kept waving her fingers and muttering, 'Think of it, here we are at the very centre of history. We can see it all happening on our doorstep.'

Indeed, it seemed to get more thrilling with every day that passed. Two mighty Royalist frigates sailed up the Colne with supplies for the garrison, only to be surprised by Parliamentary ships hiding in Brightlingsea Creek – but then you could not trust those Brightlingsea folk! The sound of the cannon made every house on the island shudder.

As in all warfare, as the summer progressed news came through that wrung the very heartstrings. In Colchester, people were having to eat dogs, cats, rats and mice – even nibbling candle ends for their mutton fat. The thatch had been taken from the roofs of houses to feed the soldiers' horses. The tower of old St Martin's Church had come tumbling to the ground in the bombardment and even the magnificent St Botolph's was reduced to its bare skeleton. Sir Thomas Fairfax did not care. 'Let them eat horseflesh and maggots till the flux increase their disease.'

Ann begged her father to start storing food in the inn's cellars to help the poor people of Colchester. He did as she asked. She had dreams of rowing the provisions over herself, but a loose tongue in a tavern is a dangerous thing and her father did not allow it. Although late at night he could be seen out on the river on some mysterious errand or other.

One sultry August day, as it grew dark, a band of Parliamentary dragoons, led by their pompous captain, with his stiff beard and even stiffer manner, arrived at the Dog & Pheasant.

'Open up your cellars, my man,' the captain demanded.

The landlord shuffled his feet uneasily and leant across the cellar door protectively. He knew how incriminating the evidence would be.

'Come on, bumpkin, do as I say.'

No movement from the door. The captain began to load his musket. Just as he raised it to his shoulder, Ann came hurtling down the stairs, shouting, 'Stop! Stop! Leave my father alone.' The captain turned towards her and there was a stench of gunpowder as his musket fired right into her face. He shook with horror as the smoke cleared and he saw the girl he had shot. He cursed the unreliability of his weapon.

'Oh! She can't be dead! Take her outside. Revive her.'

They took her outside but it was even clearer in the daylight that the life had left her body. The blood was seeping across the frills of her stiff nightdress and her face was alabaster white. The captain had no heart left for any more searches. He had not meant to kill the girl and now it seemed that her vacant eyes were staring at him accusingly. It is said that, even to this day, her white form haunts the marshes, murmuring, 'Feed my people. Take care of my people', and the wild fowl sing their elegy to the White Lady over the river Blackwater. Boatmen occasionally catch a glimpse of her on the shore and call on her for her protection.

～ BLACK SHUCK ～

'One day you'll see things you don't want to see and know things you don't want to know.'

The young teacher was startled when the old lady said this to her. The girl felt she had perhaps spoken with the arrogance of youth, but this response from the old lady was almost too much. It sounded like a curse!

A few year's later, she did indeed see something that shook her to the core. In those days she was the proud owner of a bicycle and was sometimes asked at night to go to Tollesbury to fetch the local midwife. The countryside at night then was not as dangerous a place for a lone woman as we assume it to be today, so she would do her errands quite confidently. There was just one section of the road that she found unnerving. It was the lane that led up to Gorwell Hall.

It was a perfectly ordinary lane but her father had told her that there was a man buried there with a stake through his heart. Just the sort of yarn her father would tell to frighten her on a winter's evening when his work as gardener gave him the leisure to tell such tales. If the truth be known, the Tollesbury area at that time was the haunt of smugglers, who would frequently tell a good ghost story to keep inquisitive people away from their hiding places.

On this particular January night, she was angry at being sent out after midnight. It was so cold. The grass was thick with frost and the full moon seemed to colour everything silver. She summoned all her courage for the ride along the sinister lane, and had just drawn a breath of relief at been close to the end when she sensed a hairy presence rubbing itself against the length of her bike. She was cold now with fear. She gritted her teeth and prayed that it would not knock her off her bike.

The moon had slipped out from behind a cloud so everything now looked as bright as day. She could see clearly how unkempt the creature was. Its hair was black and coarse like matting. Its eyes glowed like red embers and its tongue hung down over its jaw. The dog seemed to keep pace with her with great long strides, however fast she pedalled. Round and round the wheels went but still it kept up the pace and then suddenly, by Seabrooks Lane, the creature vanished! She was sure by now that she had seen Black Shuck, the devil dog!

She said nothing to the nurse when she got to the safety of the midwife's house and, annoyingly, the nurse sent the girl on ahead while she got her belongings together. 'You'll be all right. It's a lovely night,' was all the woman said.

'A lovely night!'

The girl clung on to this idea and saw nothing amiss until she reached Gorwell Hall Lane. To her horror, there it was again, lying in the middle of the road. Its eyes were closed but its jaws were open and she could see its hideous red tongue clearly. As carefully as she could, she edged her way round the side of the dog and rode like a soul possessed.

When she got home she did at least tell her parents what she had seen. They did their best to comfort her and sent her to bed with a warm drink, but they were anxious to go out into the lanes and hedges with lanterns to see what they could see. They saw nothing.

Unbeknown to their daughter, they reported her sighting to the squire and his gamekeeper. Surprisingly enough the gamekeeper was sympathetic and nodded his head. 'I've seen that beast myself and I tell you he's an enormous creature with drooping ears and a crimson slavering tongue. What I saw was as big as a calf, with eyes like bike lamps and it was so tall, its head was level with the floor of my trap. No wonder your girl was so frightened.' No other evidence appeared and the girl was told nothing about the investigations that had gone on in her name.

Only as an old woman did she confess that throughout her life, since that night, she had had the gift of second sight. She could foretell what might happen in the future and she could sense ghostly presences in haunted houses. It was a talent she wished she had not received, but then all sorts of things happen to those who have seen Black Shuck – sometimes good, sometimes evil – but in Essex the dog was never as fearsome as he was in Suffolk or Norfolk.

~ SPIDER ~

One of the most famous ghosts in Essex is the spirit of a man nicknamed Spider, who worked in Stock as an ostler at a pub called the Bear. As usual, it's James Wentworth Day who gives the most vivid picture of the man:

A tiny little man in dirty white breeches, a faded pink hunting coat, black velvet hunting cap, boots and stock. He was steady as a hanging judge after fourteen pints of beer, lousy as a hedge pig and swore like a Crimean trooper.

His real name was Charlie Marshall. He had no home or family and lived in the stables at the pub with the stable cat as his bed warmer. He became well known in the area for his party trick, which was to climb up the chimney in the tap room, then, covered in soot, reappear down the chimney of the bar parlour. He would get a few coppers or a free pint of beer for his trouble. Sometimes, out of a sense of mischief, he would take his time to reappear and would stay until the pub's customers lit a bunch of straw and smoked him out. His hiding place was probably a bacon loft straddling the two chimneys.

Sadly the joke went too far one Christmas Eve. He did not seem to want to come down at all. A bunch of rowdy customers tried to force him down by lighting a pile of logs. He never came, and suffocated to death. No body was found.

Later, they tried to find that bacon loft. They pushed a long pole into one of the chimneys to test the depth, only to find a large crack appearing. Panic! The crack was quickly cemented over in case the building collapsed. It didn't, but Spider's presence remained. Many people since have claimed to catch a glimpse of a ghostly figure in boots and white breeches, still teasing his tormentors.

⁓ The Moat Farm Murder ⁓

There was no doubting that Miss Camille Holland was a genteel lady of independent means, who dressed stylishly and was of the greatest respectability. Yet at the age of fifty-six and still a spinster, she was lonely. Foolishly, she put an advertisement in a matrimonial paper. She got a response. The 'captain' seemed a very spruce gentleman of great charm. Passion bloomed rapidly among the teacups of the select boarding houses where they met up. Before she realised what was happening, Camille was swept off her feet and was living 'in sin' with her lover at Brighton. Then he spoke of his great desire to live in the countryside.

'And where are you thinking of, my dearest?

'I have found a most wonderful place called Moat Farm, near the village of Clavering in rural Essex, my precious.'

Miss Holland was taken with the idea but a little grain of common sense still remained and she insisted that the farm be registered in her name only. Maybe she was already beginning to have suspicions about Samuel Herbert Dougal.

Indeed, when she arrived at Moat Farm, she could see the isolation of the place. She could feel something was not quite right. The farm stood at the end of a muddy track, only accessible by a footbridge over the moat and completely hidden behind trees. It was a place where no tradesmen called. The post was left in a box at the far end of the lane. As she arrived at the house to take up residence, she clutched her dear little dog, Jacko, to her bosom for reassurance.

The arrival of a maid called Florence may at last have seemed to add a little respectability to the arrangement, but it was the maid who began to open Camille's eyes to Dougal's true nature. You see, he had tried to kiss Florence in the kitchen. The maid was outraged. 'Oh no, sir! I'll tell the mistress. I shall have to give up my position if you continue to behave in this way.'

The mistress did not want her to leave, and that night the two women shut him out and shared the same bedroom.

A few days later Camille told the maid that she was going shopping in the trap with her 'husband'. Later that day the master came home alone, saying his wife had gone to London on the train. All very suspicious, Florence thought. She had no desire to have her reputation soiled. The next morning Florence summoned her mother, collected her wages and was gone. The captain shouted after them as they left, 'My wife's only gone for a little holiday.'

Within hours the captain had telegrammed his wife to join him at the farm. Wife, what wife? Camille, you see, had never had a ring placed on her finger. Yes, he did have a legal wife. In fact, the lady who enters our story now was wife number three. (In 1885 he had been married to a lady in Nova Scotia who died at the age of thirty-seven. Six weeks later he had married wife number two, and within the year she was dead at the age of twenty-eight.)

He was now in his fifties, a former soldier (a sergeant in the Royal Engineers) and a convicted forger who had been sentenced to twelve months' hard labour, then transferred to an asylum after he tried to commit suicide. Yet none of his neighbours seemed to have any idea of his past. The vicar's wife believed his explanation that the lady now at the farm (wife number three) was his widowed daughter, and was very grateful when given a shawl and some sheet music, unaware that they were Camille's.

Dougal himself seemed well liked as he was always a good talker, a capable shot and generous with the drinks, and for nearly four years nobody asked any serious questions about Camille's whereabouts. The fact that cheques were still appearing signed in her name seemed to silence every suspicion. Then somehow it began – clues to the real truth were emerging. It was noticed that the lady at the farm was wearing Camille's jewellery. Her dog Jacko suddenly appeared at a former landlady's house in Saffron Walden. And people wondered why Camille had left the house with no luggage.

Then the tongues really began to wag – led by wife number three, who had by now run off with another man! Not really surprising, as Dougal's record with women was baffling to say the least. He had had simultaneous affairs with two sisters and their mother. The tittle-tattle grew more heated when he was seen giving bicycle lessons to naked young women in the meadow! Later, when members of the press became involved, there was this amusing description: 'What a picture in that clayey lumpy field, the clayey lumpy girls, naked, astride that unromantic object, a bicycle, and Dougal, gross and vital, cheering on these bucolic improprieties …!'

What finally drew the police into the affair was a long list of forged cheques presented by Dougal. At last a police inquiry was opened to see if a body could be found. During the Easter of 1903, the roads around the farm were crowded with 6,000 people eager to see what progress the police were making. Then a pair of dainty button-up boots lined with wool were found and a badly decomposed body was unearthed. Only her dressmaker and shoemaker were able to recognise poor Miss Holland. A single bullet was found in her head. It was clear then that the 'captain' was the murderer. He claimed it had all been a dreadful accident caused by drinking too much brandy.

The jury were not deceived. He was found guilty of feloniously, wilfully and with malice aforethought murdering Camille Cecile Holland. On 14 July 1903 he was hanged and buried in Chelmsford Jail in an unmarked grave. He seemed to have shown few signs of conscience, although he did tell a journalist that after shooting Camille he had gone indoors for a glass of brandy. He had then gone outdoors intending to bury her but could not bring himself to do so.

Inside that place of 'bucolic improprieties', for a long time locked doors kept on opening and closing with no person visible. A piano tinkled one of those pathetic Victorian love songs whenever the house was left empty, with the music being heard right down to the gate of the farm. In the shed, there can sometimes be heard the sound of tools being thrown about, but when the tool room is examined nothing seems to have moved. After such a tragedy, it is perhaps inevitable that restless spirits are still about. Those few notes of 'Home, Sweet Home' floating through the trees are an ironic postscript to poor Camille's dreams.

~ The Tale of Kitty Canham, ~ Her Two Husbands and Three Ghosts

People continually ask me where I find my stories. The story of Kitty Canham is special as it was given to me as a gift from three ghosts. You don't believe me? Then listen to what happened.

The story begins on a hot day on the banks of the river Colne at Brightlingsea, when a group of customs officers watched a ship making slow progress on its way to Colchester. There appeared to be rather a large number of boxes aboard the ship and the customs officers' curiosity was aroused. The ship was stopped and the young man who stood in the prow was questioned. Pale, and huddled in a cloak, he gave his name as a Mr Williams from Vienna. He said that his ship had been making for Harwich when a terrible storm had come upon them, so the ship had changed direction.

Whilst John Todds, the chief customs officer, was speaking to the young man, the other customs officers were finding fine dresses, petticoats and jewels tumbling out of the boxes. One young man got impatient and drew his cutlass ready to plunge into the longest box of all, a box made of plain deal.

'No! Don't do that!' screamed Mr Williams. His face had turned even paler.

The horror in his voice made the customs officers open the box more carefully, only to discover that inside was a fine oak coffin with large silver plates containing the embalmed body of a beautiful young woman. The young man burst into tears. 'Now do you understand? That's my wife.'

'And where were you taking her?'

'I was taking her to be buried in Thorpe-le-Soken.' Grief overcame Mr Williams. He could say no more.

John Todds now thought that he might have a murder on his hands. He locked up the young man and the body of his dead wife in the Church of St Leonard's on the Hythe for the night. More investigation was needed.

The next day, an elderly couple from Thorpe-le-Soken came to the church and looked into the open coffin. They then looked at each other in amazement. 'Why, that's our vicar's wife.'

This brought fresh tears to the young man's eyes. 'It's as she said.' At last he felt he could tell the full story. He explained that he was not a Mr Williams from Vienna, but Lord Dalmeny, son of the 2nd Earl of Roseberry of Fife. He had met a beautiful girl at a party in London, and not long after that they had married and begun a four-year tour of Europe.

When they arrived at Verona, she had become very ill from a complaint then known as 'galloping consumption'. Knowing she was close to death, she had scribbled down a note that explained she was in fact a Catherine Canham, who had been married to the Revd Alexander Gough, vicar of Thorpe-le-Soken. Realising how serious a crime bigamy was, her last request was that on her death she be returned to Thorpe and buried there.

The elderly couple listened in amazement. The old man said, 'Why 'tis true. My! She was a pretty little creature. Came from a solid family of yeoman farmers. Never short of a rich admirer. Dashing young men from Mistley Park and St Osyth came a'courting her, but she decided on the vicar. Thought he might be more trustworthy! Then she gets bored. The old vicar was only interested in his dusty old books. Up she goes to London and no doubt she meets up with the likes of him,' and he pointed to Lord Dalmeny. 'The vicar's brother always said she was trouble. He warned the vicar. The brother said "she is a beautiful creature who will play you a trick" and so she has.'

The old lady reached out to pat the arm of the young lord comfortingly.

Word spread quickly and the vicar himself turned up. He was angry and ready to run a sword through the young man. Then he saw the tears in the young man's eyes and felt nothing but pity for him. Lord Dalmeny said solemnly, 'My affection for the lady is so strong that it is not only my earnest wish to attend her to the grave but to be shut up with her there.'

The vicar felt that there should at least be a magnificent funeral and so there was. Both men followed her coffin up the aisle of Thorpe-le-Soken Church for the memorial service to the place where she was to be interred under a flagstone. Neither of the men married again. Dalmeny died two years later at the age of thirty-one. His name was omitted from the peerage because of 'an irregular and romantic marriage'. The vicar survived for another twenty-two years.

Now what about the ghosts? Well, the first one I heard about was the ghost of the vicar himself. A lady who lived in the vicar's cottage and had seen his ghost told me the outline of the story. The second ghost can be found at the Bell inn at Thorpe, which overlooks the church where Kitty is buried. There were people there who said that furniture was moved about in empty rooms at night. In 1999 there was a fire at this inn, and the wall where Kitty's picture hung was blackened and fire-damaged yet the picture survived.

The third ghost is of special personal significance. He lived in my cottage and is no less a person than John Todds, the customs officer who found the ship! His epitaph in the Lady Chapel in All Saints' Church, Brightlingsea, reads:

> Farewell vain world I've known enough of thee
> And now am careless what thou sai'st of me:
> Thy smiles I court not, nor thy friends I fear:
> My race is run, my head lies quiet here:
> What fault you saw in me, take care to shun:
> And look at home, there's enough to be done.

I know what is to be done. I have another story to tell!

Seven

THE CABINET
OF CURIOSITIES

It is inevitable when you travel the byways of the Essex countryside that you come across some strange features of rustic life. Enough tales have survived to give a taste of the odder features of the old days. In those days farmers believed in helpful little folk called 'brownies'. There were others who saw them as the Devil's imps. Wise women were giving out the strangest remedies and it was a world where magic was real.

Even as late as 1928, Charlotte Mason, in her book *Essex: Its Forest, Folk and Folklore*, reported that a parson who lodged in her father's house was a wizard who had three imps. He warned the maid who waited on him never to come in the room or she would see them. When she asked 'Will they hurt me?' he said 'No'. She did in fact catch a glimpse one night and they were all the same height as the table in the room! A farm labourer saw them walk over the top of the thistles without bending their tops. This so frightened him that he moved on to work at another farm. Eventually the parson himself was told to leave for, as his landlord said, 'I would sooner have the Devil.'

Essex boasts towns that have very unique features. How did the Saffron get into Saffron Walden? What were the Coggeshall Jobs? How did seven hundred men get into a waistcoat in Maldon? Was there really an earthquake in Wivenhoe in 1884? How did strange customs such as the Dunmow Flitch develop?

As a Welshwoman, the biggest mystery to me is why there are no mountains in Essex. There's an answer to that too, as my dear friend Peter Maskens used to tell me. Always tales can be found in unlikely places. Just look out for the frolicsome fox!

– THE BAD-TEMPERED BROWNIE –

Squire Tompkins was known throughout the county for his fine stable of horses, both hunting and racing horses. This was not achieved without the help of a large gang of hardworking grooms. Young Jack Smith was delighted when he was invited to join them. What visions he had of riding the splendid beasts!

Sadly, when Jack started working there, he found that most of his time was spent cleaning the stable, polishing the tack and hauling the hay up and down the barn. His back ached, his legs ached and he was desperately tired, for his day began at dawn and there was very little time off. When he did get home he moaned and moaned about how hard his work was, but his father and mother showed no sympathy for him. They were farm labourers, who had known nothing but back-breaking labour all their lives. Only Granny smiled. 'What you need is a brownie to help you out.'

'A brownie?'

'Don't you know what a brownie is? You children know nothing! Why, they're what some folk round here call ferishers, some call boggards, some hobgoblins, and I expect you'd call them house elves. Now you get on the right side of a brownie and he'll do all your work.'

'But how do I do that?'

'Why, don't you know? Foolish child. You leave out bread and milk every night at the back door, and every night they'll come and lap it up and then they'll set to work harder than any groom I've known. But you must be careful not to let them see you.'

Jack was not sure he believed this, but, after a few days back at the never-ending work, he tried putting out the milk and bread as his grandmother had said and, do you know, within a week Jack found that all his work was getting done without any real effort on his part. He could not believe it. He had not even caught a glimpse of the brownie. It must be coming at night.

So at the next full moon, Jack hid himself in the hay loft and waited to see what happened. Sure enough, along came a little man who started to sweep up with great enthusiasm. He was an odd little creature with a shiny bald head, a face shaped like a turnip, large floppy ears, a very thin body, and arms and legs that were no better than twigs. The main thing that Jack noticed, however, was that the brownie did not wear a stitch of clothing apart from a woolly cap and muddy boots. Jack was so shocked that he let out a low whistle. The brownie looked up and saw him and was so angry that he tossed his broom up so high and so fiercely that its spikes fell all around Jack, some of them scratching his face. 'Damn you! Damn you!' it screamed and raced into the moonlight.

It never came back of course, so Jack had to go on working so hard that he got to look like an old man long before his time; but then, he should have had the good sense to show the brownie more respect.

— FUNNY MAN! FUNNY MAN! —

Strangely enough, there have been relatively recent sightings of the 'little folk', the most famous of which was at Springfield Place near Chelmsford. News of a strange sighting reached the local papers during the Second World War, when this handsome house was being used as a hostel for girls. Two of the girls complained that something sinister had touched their faces while they were sleeping on the upper floor. Their story was taken seriously and the door to the room was kept locked afterwards. The most frequent sighting was of a 'hideous little dwarf'.

This provoked a letter to the press from a Mary Petrie, whose family had previously lived there for many years. The house had always seemed peculiar, with its many trap doors, mysterious cupboards high on the wall that were never opened, long passages, and an underground chamber. Mary's relative, Lucy, said the most dramatic sighting was in a large bedroom known as the Blue Room. Her mother had taken her baby sister Nellie to sleep there because she was teething and they did not want to disturb the father. In the middle of the night, the mother was woken by the baby's chuckles and she kept saying, 'Funny man! Funny man!'

When the mother sat up she could indeed see, with his back to the fire, a hideous little man with folded arms. What an alarming creature! Back under the sheets she went. Then she decided she ought to investigate further, but by the time she had entangled herself from her bedclothes, he had gone. Baby Nellie, however, was still chortling, 'Funny man! Funny man!'

Who was he? Ghost? Goblin? One of the little folk? I'll let you decide.

~ REMEDIES OF A WISE WOMAN ~

Earache: Heat the kernel of an onion. Put it in the ear and cover with a used stocking.

Sore throat: Place the halves of a heated onion one each side of the throat and cover with a used stocking.

Nosebleed: Lower trousers and sit in a cold cowpat.

Bleeding: Staunch with a cobweb.

Burns: Apply Madonna lily leaves steeped in brandy.

Sores: Apply a mite of mouldy cheese.

Measles: Drink a brew of marigold flowers followed by a draught of good ale.

Whooping cough: Skin and toast a freshly caught mouse and eat hot.

Coughs and colds: Rub back and front of chest with warm goose fat or tallow. Give a sup of blackcurrant tea or mead.

Congestion of the lungs: Swallow live jumping jakes (small frogs) to suck up the phlegm. (There was a near tragedy when the jake was found to be too large for the child to swallow, but the legs were sticking out and it was removed in time.)

Chilblains: Beat with holly to let out the bad blood and apply warm goose fat or tallow.

Rheumatism: Back up against a hive and be well stung by the bees. A complete cure.

Gout: Apply a hot mash made from ground elder leaves.

~ How Saffron Got into Saffron Walden ~

Saffron is a graceful lilac flower that blooms in the autumn. It is grown for the stigmas, which are a deep orange colour and when dried can be used as a dye or as a medicine, and now most frequently in cooking. The plant originates in Greece and Asia Minor; the following is Richard Hakluyt's explanation for how Saffron came to England:

> It is reported at Saffron Walden that a pilgrim purporting to do good to his country, stole an head of Saffron, and hid the same in his palmer's staff, which he had made hollow before of purpose and so he brought this root into this realm, with venture of his life, for had he been caught taking it from its country of origin, he would have been in danger of his life.

Saffron was used in Persian carpet weaving and enriched the medieval English textile trade, but there were some strange warnings from herbalists. According to one, an overdose could cause people to die laughing. But for many it simply made them happy. An old saying alludes to a cheerful person as someone who has 'slept in a bag of saffron'!

The plant is an attractive shape so the drawings of it appear everywhere in saffron Walden – in the pargeting on the sides of houses, in the town's coat of arms, and even carved in the spandrels of a stone arch in the beautiful parish church. Today saffron is not grown any more on a commercial scale, but the variety of designs it inspired for pargetting (decorative external plasterwork) has made the modern town very picturesque.

Maybe the person who plastered the design on the walls of the old Sun Inn had tasted a little of the magical saffron. The design appears to show the story of Tom Hickathrift and the Wisbech giant. These two splendid giants had a thrilling battle. The Wisbech giant used a club; Tom used an axle from his dray as his weapon, and a wheel to act as shield. Tom won and savagely severed the head of his rival – which he fully deserved, for the giant's lair had been full of severed heads, like rows of conkers. Tom was bound to win for, in the tradition of giant stories, he had a widowed mother, no money and was not very bright. Hurray for the simple man!

~ THE COGGESHALL JOBS ~

The people of Coggeshall are remarkably good-natured, and have been the butt of many jokes for centuries. John Ray, the famous botanist of Braintree, used to repeat this curious little rhyme:

> Braintree for the pure and Bocking for the poor:
> Coggeshall for the jeering town,
> And Kelvedon for the whore.

An even stranger tradition was a 'Coggeshall job'. This was a joke where a ridiculous answer was given to a sensible problem, e.g.

Q: How should the farmer ripen his plums?
A: Light a fire under the trees.

Q: What should the child do with his wheelbarrow now his dog has bitten it?

A: Chain the wheelbarrow to a tree in case it gets rabies.

Q: An old lady's house has been flooded. What should she do to stop the waters reaching upstairs?

A: Send for a carpenter to take down the staircase.

Q: A window cleaner has found his ladder is too short. What should he do?

A: Cut off the bottom rung and stick it on the top.

Q: The drill sergeant of the local regiment has found that his men do not know their left foot from their right foot. How can he keep them marching in good order?

A: Tie a wisp of straw to the right leg and a wisp of hay to the left leg and then shout, 'Hay! Straw! Hay! Straw! Hay! Straw!'

~ The Amazing Waistcoat ~

Every town boasts a character that is larger than life. In 1750 they did not come any bigger than 'Great Bright' or, to give him his proper name, Edward Bright of Maldon. It was reported that at his death, at the age of twenty-nine, he was 5ft 9in tall, weighed nearly 42 stone, measured 5ft 6in around the chest and 6ft 11in around the belly.

The parish register recorded that when he died:

A way was cut though the wall and staircase of his house to let the coffin down into the shop: it was drawn upon a carriage to the church and slid upon rollers to the vault made of brickwork, and interred with the help of a triangle and pulley. He was a very honest tradesman, a facetious companion, comely in his person, affable in his temper, a tender father and a valuable friend.

It is comforting to know that when he died his fine qualities were recognised by all his friends and relations – but even they must have puzzled about how he reached such a size. One explanation was that when he was ten years old he helped his family's fortunes by acting as a post boy. The ride back and forth from Maldon to Chelmsford gave him a vigorous appetite, so when he got home he would tuck into all sorts of stodgy food – and today we know only too well what stodgy food does to a person!

Slowly and surely he began to grow bigger and bigger. Luckily, at twelve years old, he was apprenticed to a Mr Pattison. As he reached his twenties he was able to run his own grocery and chandler's shop in Maldon High Street. On and on his girth increased. There were still large meals, but, even more dangerously, Mr Bright had developed a passion for strong beer. By the age of twenty-two he weighed 30 stone! His daily intake of liquor was a gallon of small beer and half a pint of wine. On his visits to London on business, his huge bulk attracted 'the gazing stock and admiration of all people'. Eventually his health was affected and he grew breathless and walked with difficulty, but he managed to survive by being bled. Then, in the November of 1750, he met his end through catching typhus. One comment at his passing was that 'his corpulence so overpowered his strength that his life was a burden and his death a deliverance'.

His friends, his pregnant wife and five children may have mourned his passing, but the general public made him the butt of countless jokes and a curious sort of local pride. His fame spread, mainly because of a notorious gamble between two local shopkeepers, Mr Codd and Mr Hants, at the Black Bull tavern. Mr Codd maintained that five hundred men could be buttoned up in Mr Bright's green baize waistcoat without breaking a single stitch. Mr Hants said that was impossible. On 1 December 1750 the matter was put to trial. Amazingly, it was actually found that seven hundred men fitted neatly into the waistcoat. 'Ridiculous!' you say. Oh no it's not! You must have forgotten the old way for dividing up Essex's administrative districts. It was in 'hundreds', so the seven men who got in the waistcoat came from the Dengie Hundred. This qualified them to be seven 'hundred' men. See, it's simple. Take a look at the sculpture in the middle of Maldon High Street behind the King's Head pub and you will see how it was done. Although, on a recent television programme, Michael Portillo tried to squeeze seven people into a replica of the famous waistcoat and the attempt was not wholly successful.

~ My Hat! ~

(A tale from the 1884 earthquake)

Mrs Cuthbert was a proud woman. She liked everything to be neat and tidy, and clearly wished that Mr Cuthbert was a great deal more organised than he was. He was particularly annoying in the morning. He would get up early enough but then he would fritter his time away reading the newspaper and eating his breakfast. So in the end he would find himself in a great rush, for he needed to be out of the house before 9 a.m. Mrs Cuthbert always had the fire lit in the parlour and the breakfast dishes washed before he reached his workplace, which was the Wivenhoe shipyard.

This particularly wonderful April morning she was looking forward to washing the lace curtains. She was famous for having curtains of the purest white. It had been raining for several days, but today the sky was blue and the sun was shining, although there wasn't much of a breeze.

Mr Cuthbert was agitated. He had got into his painting overalls and put his brushes in his bag, but he could not find his brown derby hat anywhere. It was a battered old hat yet he was fond of it. Lord Alfred Paget himself had seemed impressed by it. Rumour had it that this distinguished man was in town that day. He was coming to check his yacht, the *Santa Cecilia*, after its crossing from America. The boat was equally important to Mr Cuthbert. After all, he had painted it that beautiful dark blue and it still looked as trim as the day he had done it.

Then Mr Cuthbert heard the loudest noise he had ever heard. It sounded like a boiler exploding! He was rocked off his feet. As he fell over backwards, he saw the walls of his hallway buckle and creak. The ceiling above seemed to open up like a gaping mouth and then through it came a crashing chimney. Bricks were smashing and skidding at all angles. One group of bricks, still held together by cement, cracked into Mr Cuthbert's exposed shins. It hurt! Worst of all was that he had no idea what was happening. Was this the end of the world? Outside he could hear the cries of other souls in terror. He rolled over, clutching his knees with shaking fingers.

In the kitchen, Mrs Cuthbert was open-mouthed with shock as she saw cracks appearing through the walls, glass from the windows splintering everywhere, and outside the roof tiles cascading in an unending shower of broken slate.

'Harold, are you all right?'

She heard a moan from the hallway. Without thinking of the danger, she ran to pull her husband away from harm. As she got him to his feet, they both saw through the open doorway of the parlour the other chimney falling into the fireplace. It sent coals scattering across the carpet, so that flames went flickering across the room. In the light from the flames, Mr Cuthbert saw his brown derby hat on the little round table where he had left it the night before.

'My hat!' he said pathetically, trying to struggle away from her to go into the sitting room to get his hat. She was a woman with strong arms from all the laundry she did and she had an even stronger will. As she hauled him outside onto the doorstep, she muttered, 'Damn your hat, you silly old fool. Just be glad you are still alive.'

~ A Lost Dream ~

It was a dream the old woman had nursed for eighteen years. Every night she saw it as she slipped into sleep. She dreamt of a treasure buried near her rundown cottage on the Rochford Hall estate. The treasure never actually became visible. She just caught a glimpse of something golden buried in the ground underneath a large stone arch. Of course, she had a clear idea of where the arch was, but she was too nervous to mention it to anyone or to go look for herself.

As she got older and older she got poorer and poorer. Even a few golden coins would make it possible to live into a far more comfortable old age. 'I must ask him for permission to search there,' she thought to herself, and at last she mentioned it to the tenant farmer on whose land her cottage stood.

He laughed, 'I can't give you permission to dig. You'll have to ask the Lord of the Manor. He might give you permission but, knowing that greedy old devil, I am sure he'll make you promise to hand over anything you might find.'

By now the old woman had become so determined that when the Lord of the Manor came to visit the estate she was waiting for him. She would ask. She would! Flinging herself on her knees in front of him, she begged to be allowed to dig in the spot which her dreams had revealed to her. Even more bravely, she asked to be allowed to keep anything she might find. I am not sure whether he was in a particularly sunny temper that day or whether he was a genuinely kind man; he not only gave her permission to dig but he actually lent her one of his men and a pickaxe to dig the ground for her.

It was hard work. The labourer sighed and then, to his disgust, he dug straight into an enormous stone that seemed totally immovable. The Lord of the Manor sent another man to help, but it didn't look as though they would ever find that archway she had seen in her dreams. In floods of tears she went to the Lord of the Manor and told him it was a lost cause. He had to admit she was right and gave her a purse of coins to cheer her. They were only pennies but they were enough to buy her bread and cheese for several days.

Twenty years later, the old woman had died and a stranger riding past her cottage found in the dust of the road a golden ring with a blue stone which had the marks of a spade on it. He put it in his pocket with a smile. 'Someone's lost dream,' he thought to himself.

~ THE DUNMOW FLITCH ~

The Bible says that 'the price of a good woman is above rubies'. The prior of Dunmow in 1104 was a little more down-to-earth when he decided that the reward of a happy marriage was a flitch of bacon. It was a prize the wise prior gave to Reginald Fitzwalter and his wife when they came to him dressed as humble folk and asked him to bestow a blessing on them after a year and a half of marriage. Fitzwalter then revealed his true identity and gave some of his land to the priory, on the condition that the prior continued to reward a flitch to any couple married as happily as himself and his wife.

Any husband competing for this splendid prize had to claim that he and his wife had not repented of their marriage (either sleeping or waking) for a year and a day. The happy couple then took an oath before the prior and convent and the whole town, humbly kneeling on two pointed stones, and then the husband and wife were paraded on a chair through the town. So remarkable was this ceremony that it was mentioned in *Piers Ploughman* and in the Wife of Bath's tale in *The Canterbury Tales*. After the Dissolution, it became a purely secular affair.

In 1751 it was a very merry occasion. Anne Shakeshaft proudly proclaimed that she had never said a cross word during her seven years of marriage to Thomas, a weaver from Wethersfield. A jury of six men and six women found by reason of their quiet, peaceable, tender and loving cohabitation that the couple were fit and qualified to receive the bacon.

Five thousand people attended and bright yellow ribbons were worn at the presentation. The jollity spilled over into the evening, when there was dancing and cards at the Saracen's Head. Anne and Thomas made the best of their good fortune by selling the slices of bacon they had won to several ladies and gentlemen present who were 'whimsically merry on the occasion'. Anne was so pleased that she said she wished she had married her husband sooner.

Harrison Ainsworth, the Victorian novelist, revived the custom as a civil event. He wrote a novel in which the publican of an inn known as the Flitch of Bacon married a succession of wives in order to find the perfect one.

The trial had a special charm in 1912, maybe because a local journalist recorded it so vividly. He said a jury was assembled according to tradition, with six bachelors and six unmarried women, '… one half of which would drive many men to crime for the sake of being tried by six girls so pretty and charmingly gowned'. There were two trumpeters in scarlet uniform, a court clerk, a court crier, a council for claimants and a council for the bacon. The judge was suitably impressed and actually said the couple's marriage was like 'an Iliad in a nutshell'. This was obviously a romantic turn of phrase. The husband, however, felt able to say of his wife: 'It's all her. There never was a cloud so black that she couldn't see sunshine aback of it.'

The journalist noticed the wife was more nervous, and he said of her:

As the little lady stepped up to the stand, her presence was sufficient testimony. Steady eyes shone out of a calm face, framed in its band of silver hair. Eight children had grown to maturity in the light of those eyes and for thirty-six years she had accommodated Mr Smith's tobacco smoking, political ways. When asked how it was she and her husband had not quarrelled in the past year she answered 'we are all the world to each other, him and me. There is nothing to quarrel about.'

Here was a couple worthy of the flitch, and perhaps their story shows why the strange medieval ritual continues. The ceremony is held every leap year and each couple have a counsel to defend their claim. Successful couples are carried shoulder-high in the ancient Flitch Chair to the Market Place, where they take an oath kneeling on pointed stones. The chair and stones are kept at the priory church at Little Dunmow. The ceremony itself is held at Great Dunmow. Couples now come from far afield to compete. There is something very engaging about such faith in married love in our cynical age.

⌐ The Last Mountain in Essex ⌐

(A story told by Peter Maskens)

Sir Gwillum de Donker was a bold Flemish knight who held much land in Essex. He took as much as he could from the people: their money, their animals and their crops. If anyone complained, he had them thrown into the dungeons. As he grew older he began to fear that he would not get into heaven. 'Promise me,' he said to his wife, 'that you will build a monastery and fill it with monks to pray that I may go to heaven. For I have been a wicked man starving the people.'

After Sir Gwillum died, she kept her promise and built the monastery. Soon it was filled with monks who took turns to pray for him twenty-four hours a day. The monastery was built at Peldon, right by the last mountain in Essex. A large town grew up beside the monastery and became known as Abberton. There was one small monk called Thomas, who nobody thought much of because he was so shy. The abbot put Thomas in charge of their small flock of goats and had him dressed in the roughest clothing.

'There, that will do for you Thomas, you're not very bright, you can talk to the goats.'

So every day Thomas would take the goats up on the mountain to feed. The other monks thought it a joke. 'Look at him,' they used to say, 'when he walks up the mountain no one can tell which is Thomas and which is a goat.' Thomas didn't mind what they said; he felt he was being useful and no one ever refused his goats' cheese. All day long Thomas would sit with the goats until it was time to return to the monastery for prayers and supper.

The years rolled by and eventually Lady de Donker died. Her relatives came and did not want the monastery. They sold the land, the houses and the animals and moved away. The abbot and the monks had no money, and no one was willing to take on a large monastery. The abbot called a meeting of all the monks and asked them to think of ways to raise money. All the goats had been sold, but Thomas still climbed the mountain every day to sit on the rocks at the top and think of how he could help. It was always warm up there on the rocks, even in midwinter.

One day he decided to look beneath the rocks to see where the warmth came from. He levered a few rocks away and found there was a small hole, up from which came a draught of warm air. He rolled more rocks away until he could see a deep hole, just like a rough-sided chimney going down into the mountain. He thought the hole would not go very far, so he climbed in and started clambering down. It was much deeper than he expected and he began to get a bit afraid, but he said a prayer and carried on.

After a while he stopped and looked up. There above him was the sky, just like a small round hole in the darkness. He looked down and there in the distance was a slight red glow. He worried that there was a dragon or a wizard waiting for him but he said some more prayers and carried on. He had gone too far to turn back and he had to know what was there.

Down, down he went, with the air getting warmer and the glow getting brighter. He tried shouting a few times but the only answer was the echo of his own voice. At last he came to the bottom of the tunnel, which he expected to be a cavern, but it only opened up into a smaller chamber not much bigger than a cupboard. On the floor was a large, glowing ruby-red jewel. Thomas reached out and felt the warmth radiating from the jewel. He was a bit frightened and touched it with his finger. It was hot but did not burn. He half expected a blast from a wizard or a dragon, but nothing happened.

A rumble in his tummy reminded him that he had not eaten since breakfast. That decided it. He picked up the jewel, put it in a fold of his habit and tightened his rope belt over it. Climbing back took much longer than he had thought. He had to rest several times on the way and when he climbed out of the tunnel it was getting dark. The gatekeeper at the monastery told Thomas that he was in serious trouble for being so late and there was no supper left. Thomas demanded to see the abbot. That, he was told, would get him into even more trouble. But he insisted and refused to give a reason.

At last Thomas was shown into the abbot's room. It was very cosy with a nice fire burning in the hearth, and there was a smell of roast chicken and rich wine in the air. The abbot could not remember a time when a lowly monk had spoken to him. Talking with monks was usually left to others. Thomas said nothing but pulled the glowing jewel out of his habit and placed it in the middle of the table. No one moved or spoke until Thomas' belly rumbled loudly. The abbot tried to speak but all he could manage was a squeaky little voice. 'Er, Thomas, er, would you like to sit down and have something to eat?'

Thomas did like to, very much, so he tucked into the abbot's supper as fast as he could. Hours later, after Thomas had answered all the questions and had drunk all the wine, he was helped to bed. In the morning a messenger was sent to the King, who happened to be hunting not far away at Havering-atte-Bower. The King came as fast as he could on a lathered and exhausted horse. After he overcame his surprise and delight, the King claimed the jewel as his own but offered to support the monastery for the rest of his life, which he did.

Thomas was the hero; the smallest and least clever monk had saved them all. He had a new room with a fire in winter and lived to a ripe old age. But the mountain was never the same. Its heart had been taken and it died. It shrank smaller and smaller until there was nothing left of it. It carried on shrinking down into its roots and, as it did, the hole filled with water. To this day it is still shrinking and filling with water, and we now use it for our drinking water and call it Abberton Reservoir. This was the last mountain in Essex, and we hope now that it will save us from droughts.

~ TALLY HO! ~

The villagers of Bradwell always enjoyed it when the rector rode out with his pack of foxhounds. He had a good seat on a horse and had grown to know the locality really well. The gentry who rode with him liked him because he seemed a sensible fellow who got on with solving practical problems. Sir Henry Bate Dudley was more involved in taking on the responsibilities of a squire and a magistrate than that of a clergyman. He did at least make sure the churchyard was tidy – and actually cleared out the pigs after they had rooted around for so many years. His real achievement, though, had been overseeing the improvement of roads and draining the marshes.

The younger men, of course, used to gossip in the taverns about the rector's nickname in his younger days. He was known as the 'fighting parson'. And how did he get his name? Well, he fought duels. One duel was fought with pistols and one duel with bare knuckles. They were fought to rescue the reputation of various ladies of fashion. Such gallantry! There was a rumour that he had done a spell in the King's Bench Prison for being outspoken about the Duke of Richmond. 'All power to him for having the courage to speak his mind,' most said.

Now the ladies liked him for other reasons. Here was a man of elegance and wit who entertained with fine dinners where guests could include the artists Thomas Gainsborough and William Hogarth, and the actors Sarah Siddons and David Garrick. How he had improved Bradwell Lodge! He had added the most fashionable of extensions, claiming it was needed to keep a watch out for smugglers! (He was actually trying to set Gainsborough up with a rather fine art studio.)

Sadly the pretty ladies would not join the hunt on this particular day, not even his lovely wife and her actress sister. Just as well, for, the hounds found a sprightly vixen who led the most incredible run over field and marshes. They followed as far as the hamlet of Creeksea and wondered for a moment if the fox was planning to take the ferry across the Crouch! Not she. She was climbing up the buttress of the church to the roof. Creeksea Church was not in good order then. Six hounds followed, baying with excitement, and then Sir Henry himself was up on the roof. Sadly the poor vixen was too exhausted to put up much of a fight. Sir Henry said, 'Well, we could not have let her go without benefit of clergy.'

A crowd gathered below, mainly servants from Creeksea Place, the local manor. Some felt sorry for the fox, but the bulk of the crowd were cheering, 'Hurrah for Sir Henry!' They had a soft spot for a fighting parson in those parts … as they did on Foulness Island, which also boasted a fighting foxhunting parson. Thomas Archer had a much rougher congregation to lead. The population of Foulness in the early nineteenth century consisted mainly of bare-fist fighters, horse stealers and smugglers. Archer fitted in perfectly. Problematic parishioners were sorted out with fist fights. He smoked a white clay pipe that he left in a niche in the porch ready to light again after a service was over. His usual dress was a blue frock coat, white corduroy breeches, grey worsted stockings and a red night cap. If there was a possibility of a hunt after a service, he quite often wore his red hunting jacket under his surplice.

The best-known story about him was that once, while conducting a wedding service, he suddenly shouted 'Tally Ho!' as he glimpsed, through the open door of the church, a fox racing by, followed by the hunt. He thought he was quite the rider and chose the most difficult routes to show off his hunting skills. Sometimes he regretted it, as he was often badly injured when taking some of the more difficult jumps. He actually broke his leg while jumping the church stile. Susannah, his wife, was known as 'Pug' and must have been a remarkably patient lady to put up with the old rapscallion. Maybe the odd fragments of poetry he wrote about her pacified her.

Eight

Holy Ways

There are many men and women who are celebrated in Essex for venturing out on exciting spiritual journeys. For instance, an exciting archaeological discovery was made after a road-widening scheme in Prittlewell near Southend. Here was the burial chamber of a Saxon king, who had evidently been searching for new inspiration in Christian ideals. Hopefully the splendid treasures unearthed will soon be on proud display in an appropriate home in a museum in Southend. These are treasures that all of Essex should see.

Of all the Christian missionaries who came to convert the East Saxons, St Cedd was the most famous, and his wonderful stone chapel at Bradwell is one of the most evocative of East Anglian buildings. Sadly the Dissolution destroyed the religious houses of Essex, yet interesting stories still survive. Chich Abbey was linked with the strange tale of headless St Osyth. And, at Coggeshall Abbey, Abbot Ralph was a remarkable tale-teller himself. Many artists have been inspired by his story of 'The Wild Man of Orford'.

The Reformation was a turbulent time, with Queen Mary I burning Protestants at the stake. (Any burnings at the stake in Essex refer to these persecutions and not to witches, whose punishment was to be hanged.) This was followed by Elizabeth I forcing Catholic priests into hiding. By the seventeenth century a strong Puritan faith had taken hold in parts of Essex, and many people felt so strongly about the way they worshipped that they set off for the greater freedom of the New World.

⁓ THE MERSEA BARROW ⁓

They have not left us yet, the ghosts of the Romans. Their presence still haunts certain parts of Essex and especially Mersea Island, for this is the place where the Romans sent people to recuperate after illness, or to relax. It is here on the Strood – the causeway that links Mersea Island to the mainland – that the best-known ghost of all, the centurion, marches on and on and on towards the hill they call the Barrow. Sometimes it is the clattering of his armour that people hear and sometimes it is a presence that is sensed.

It was Mrs Jane Pullen, the landlady of the Peldon Rose, who described most vividly an encounter with the ghost of the centurion:

> He came down off the Barrow Hills. The steady tramp of a man's feet, like a soldier marching and he caught up with me and walked all the way down to the Strood.
>
> I could see no one, yet the feet were close behind me, as near as I could have touched him. I bopped down to look along the road in the moonlight, yet no one was there. Still the feet kept on.

I walked along the road till I came to a man I knew. He was all of a-tremble. He shook like a leaf.

'I can hear him,' he said 'but where is he? I can't see anyone.'

'Keep along with me' I said to the man 'and no harm will come to you. 'Tis only one of those old Romans come out of the Barrows to take his walk.'

Mrs Pullen was not frightened for she declared she put her trust in God. 'And when you do that, naught can harm you. Besides, those old Romans do you no harm.'

Maybe she had come to a conclusion similar to that of the archaeologist Hazzledine Warren, who dug out the barrow in 1912. He thought that there was a ghost in the mound, but 'not a ghost possessing any notable or distinctive personality'. Sadly he never explained what ghostly presence he might have heard or seen.

We do know that Hazzledine Warren thought the barrow was built between AD 60 and 96 for a person of great importance, maybe the leader of a Celtic tribe who lived on the island. He dug a central shaft that connected with a short passageway. At first he found nothing but pottery, flints and oyster shells, and then came the excitement of finding a beautiful green glass burial urn in a lead box which contained cremated remains. Amazingly the urn was transported by one of the rather ramshackle cars of the time to Colchester Castle, where it was removed from its tight-fitting casket without a single scratch. Sadly we still don't know if those cremated bones belonged to a man or a woman.

We storytellers, of course, have our own ideas. The Essex Storytellers have decided that the barrow was the site of a great love story between a Celtic chief and his Roman wife who died in childbirth. A Roman centurion had also loved the lady dearly, and now haunts the site of her death.

In the following extract, Andy Jennings has imagined the walk of the centurion across the Strood. Andy saw the centurion as a sad man who had returned to the island to marry his love too late. And as the Roman approaches the barrow, he hears the sound of her funeral …

He hears the funerary mourners chanting, calling the spirits to rest. The sound carries on the wind.

He falters. He leaves, his head down. The rain hides his tears again. He rides on until he notices water on either side. He realises then he is on the Strood, the causeway between the mainland and the island. He is sick of killing, sickened that death has followed him here. He is tired of it all, wanting an escape.

His horse pauses and snorts. Tired and sweating, the mare shivers in the cooling twilight. The man dismounts, distracted. He's looking back. Through the fog, lights from Camulodunum can be seen. He can see faces, recognisable faces, his fallen comrades! Their bitter faces appear in the cold mist and bar his way. They shake their gory locks as if to say 'do not go back there'.

So he turns, but his eyes fill with tears at the sight of the island. His mind is confused. The fog in his head matches the cold mist that rises around him as the sluggish tide inexorably fills the channel. By the time he registers the cold, he is ankle deep in water, the distance to land too great. He awaits his doom. The pull of the water increases. He slips, numb to everything but his own pain and loss. He sinks, dragged down by his own armour, a heart that died before it had stopped beating. Once more he is lost.

The mystery of the barrow has haunted many people's imaginations. Sabine Baring-Gould invented the legend of the Viking lovers, which was no doubt inspired by his love of Norse legends.

In his novel *Mehalah* he calls the mound 'Grimes Dyke'. In the tale, two brothers fall in love with the beautiful sister of St Osyth:

> They brought the girl back to Mersea and then each would have her for their own. So the brothers fell out over whose she should be, and all their love turned to jealousy and their brotherhood turned to enmity and it came about they fought with their long swords over who should have the maid. They fought and smote and hacked one another till their armour was broken and their flesh was cut off and their blood flowed away and by nightfall they were both dead. There the Danes drew their ship up to the top of the hill above the Strood and they placed the maid in the hold with a dead brother on either side of her, in his tattered harness, sword in hand, and they heaped a mountain over them and buried them all, the living and the dead together.
>
> When the new moon appears, the flesh grows on their bones and the blood staunches, and the wounds close, and the breath comes back behind their ribs. When the moon is full, they rise in the ship's hold and fall upon one another, and if you listen at full moon on the hoe you can hear the brother fighting below in the heart of the barrow. You can hear them curse and cry out and you can hear the clash of their swords. But when the moon wanes the sounds grow fainter, their armour falls to bits, their flesh drops away, the blood oozes out of all the hacked veins and at last all is still. Then when there is no moon, you can hear the maid mourning and sobbing: you can hear her distinctly till the new moon reappears and then she is hushed, for the brothers are recovering for a new fight. This will go on month after month, year after year, till one conquers the other and wins the maid; but that will never be for the brothers are of the same age and equally strong and equally resolute.

After the archaeological dig, a tunnel was dug by the mound to make it possible for visitors to see the tomb's chamber at the barrow's heart … and maybe hear the echo of whatever ghosts are there. In 2012 there have been grants to prevent any deterioration of the structure.

~ BURIAL OF A KING ~

Around 1,400 years ago, a king of the East Saxons died and was taken to his burial chamber by his sons. They laid him in his simple wooden coffin. It was a chamber 13ft square, dug into the ground and lined with wood. Around him they placed all the treasure that he would need in the next life, for they knew no better. They were pagans, and thought he must go to the afterlife with the same magnificence he had known in this life. They were proud of the fact that in their family's genealogy was the name of Seaneting, an ancient god of the Saxons.

As they entered the burial chamber, it was like entering the hospitality of the King's own hall. There was no one better than their father at welcoming people from many lands, and no one who received better presents from their guests. Oh! Surely in the afterlife their father would feast among the gods themselves in just such a splendid hall.

So from the chamber's wooden walls they hung all manner of copper bowls and a huge cauldron. On the floor were copper buckets. There were the most lovely glass drinking vessels; one shone a rich blue and another shone a watery green. How beautifully those flower-embossed glasses glowed when they were lifted to the light.

And how well the sons remembered their father, sitting on his folding chair! Always laughing as he brought out the gaming pieces and dice. Yet there had been a need for caution. Always there must be a sword and shield within reach in case raiders came. Ah, best of all, the sweet lyre kept so carefully in a leather case. How sweetly he would strum to the stories of elves and goblins, dwarves and dragons, gods and heroes.

However, as the King had drawn closer to death he had seemed to be searching for something. He had asked questions of Christian missionaries about the purpose of life. He had listened to many different missionary stories but he felt no story ran truer than one that had come from the North. This story had said:

> When we compare the present life of man on earth with that time of which we have no knowledge, it seems to me like the swift flight of a single sparrow through the banqueting hall, where you sit at dinner on a winter's day with your thegns and counsellors. In the midst, there is a comforting fire to warm the hall. Outside the storms of winter rain or snow are raging.
>
> The sparrow flies quickly through one door of the hall, and out through another. While he is inside, he is safe from the winter storms; but after a few moments of comfort, he vanishes from sight into the wintry world from which he came. Even so, man appears on earth for a little while: but of what went before this life or what follows, we know nothing. Therefore if this teaching has brought any more certain knowledge, it seems only right that we should follow it.

The King had come to the understanding that this was the Christian teaching that best solved the mystery of life and death.

There are clues that this was how the Saxon king thought. At the burial chamber, a Coptic bowl was found in which to wash men's feet like a Christian monk, and there was a silver spoon like those used in the Christian communion service. There were even two gold Latin crosses. These had been placed over his eyes at the moment of death. There were also hollow golden buckles in which to hide the sacred relics of a saint. His whole style of dressing was simple, like someone thinking only of serious purposes. His sons, however, had been determined to see him buried with purses of gold. After all, they might be needed to pay the ferryman of the river which led to the Other Life.

Even today we are not sure what happens when we pass through the great door of the hall at the far end of life. Will we need to pay the ferryman or should our eyes be closed, ready to welcome the radiance of heaven?

⁓ The Homecoming ⁓

It was AD 655 when the boy jumped out of a boat on the beach near the chapel of St Peter-on-the-Wall. People came out of their huts and ran to welcome him, but he ignored them and went straight into the darkened chapel. No one followed him except an elderly monk. They were in the chapel for well over half an hour. As the news of his arrival spread, more and more people came out to wait for the boy. They wanted so much to hear his news. The hubbub of chatter grew louder and louder.

'Do you think they got there in time?'

'Why has the boy come home alone?'

'Perhaps he never got there at all. Perhaps they sent him home halfway along the road. It's a very long way for a twelve-year-old boy to go. They say that the North Country is a dangerous place. Anything could have got the brethren. The forests are full of wolves and evil men they say.'

'More like the plague got them. We knew the bishop was sick when our monks went to see him.' A girl shivered at the thought and went indoors.

At last the monk emerged from the chapel and held his hand up for their attention. They could tell immediately by his face that Bishop Cedd was dead. They were not ready for the next piece of news. The thirty monks who had left Bradwell to be with their bishop had died of the plague too. The boy, at least, had survived.

Nobody knew quite what to say to him. Some did touch his arm as he emerged out of the chapel. Then at last the boy smiled. He had caught a glimpse of his mother. He ran to her and fell into her arms. His father, fresh from fishing, stepped back a little. He still wore the pagan charm of Thor's silver hammer around his neck, for he had never been sure of these strange Christian ways. Not everybody in the community had been converted to Christianity by Bishop Cedd. He could be very hard on men who followed the old ways. He had even spoken harshly to King Sigeberht about the company he kept.

The fisherman had never felt comfortable in the bishop's presence. He had never wanted his son to go north with the thirty monks to visit their dying bishop. What good could that have done? He was relieved that at least the boy was safe.

More and more people began to crowd around them. The boy pulled his father away from the other people; they went to the beach and looked at the chapel in the dying light of the day. 'I had to come home. It's beautiful here. So remote from anything else,' the boy said. 'All that purple salting and silver sea make it magical. There's nothing in the North like this. I don't even mind the Roman ghosts.' Father and son laughed as they remembered the day they had found the bones of a wild boar and a knife, and the pottery of the Roman soldiers. The boy had been so frightened; now it was he who was so brave. He took his father back inside the chapel.

His father had always been a little nervous of it, but even he had to admit the building of the chapel had been a remarkable achievement. So clever to have used the stones of the ruins of the Roman fort of Othona, which had once stood in this very place. It was a little dark, for there were few windows, just bare walls. In the joy of the homecoming, however, they both felt the aura of the place and were content, as people are today who find their way over the marshes to this special centre of East Anglian spirituality.

⚊ The Strange Case of the Headless Saint ⚊

Stories about the medieval lives of saints rarely grip a modern audience. It is almost impossible to tell the story of St Osyth to our generation of disbelievers, yet it has its fascination. I will tell it in its simplest form and I guarantee it still has the ability to amaze for all sorts of reasons. Make of it what you will.

Once, when there were seven Anglo-Saxon kingdoms, King Fritheward ruled the kingdom of the East Angles with his wife Walburga, a Mercian princess. Fritheward was the first Christian ruler of the East Angles. When his daughter Osyth was born, he sent her to St Modwenna to receive a proper education.

One day, the girl was sent to take a book to the saint, but she was blown off a bridge by a gust of wind and fell into the river. Fortunately, an angel directed St Modwenna to the exact spot where the girl had fallen. Three shepherds confirmed that they had seen a girl on the bridge and that they had called, 'Osyth! Osyth! Osyth! Come back to us we pray.' Down in the rushing waters the girl's body bobbed up, and to everyone's delight her head rose above the water and her eyes opened. 'Praise be to God! The child lives,' they cried.

Osyth, in fact, lived to be a lovely young woman. Her parents were delighted when she was betrothed to Sighere, King of Essex. This did not please the girl herself, for in her heart she wished to remain a virgin and have only Christ as her lord. Her wishes came true in the strangest way. At their wedding feast a magnificent stag passed the house. Sighere was such an enthusiastic huntsmen that he could not resist it. With a blast on his horn he summoned his followers, mounted his steed, and off the party went to the woods to hunt. They left Osyth and her ladies behind, but she was not dismayed. She realised that it was the will of God and took herself and her ladies to a religious house where she could live the life of a nun. We do not know how successful the hunt was, but King Sighere apparently did not resent Osyth's new life. In fact, he made it possible for her to build a convent at the village known as Chich and she became its first abbess.

All went well until Viking boats were seen sailing up the nearby creek. A party of fierce warriors, led by Inguar and Hubba, disembarked at the creek. Obviously they had evil in their hearts. They sacked the convent and then came upon the lovely Osyth, standing by a fountain in the woods. Their leaders demanded that she come to their ship. She saw the savagery in their eyes. She feared their brutality and that they would ask her to worship their gods. She refused to move. Immediately they brought the full weight of their broadswords down on her vulnerable neck and her head was severed cleanly from her body.

Yet the grace of God was with her. Cradling her head in her arms, she made her way for three furlongs to the church and knocked pitifully with her bloodstained hands on the door. There was no answer. It was locked! She fell dead on the threshold. Then, where her head had rested, it seemed as though the earth itself wept at her fate. The clear flowing waters that sprung up were to provide solace to much of the community.

The spring itself had a reputation for healing disease and impotency. So it was that Osyth at last became *Saint* Osyth because of the many miracles for which she was responsible. A tradition grew up: in those days, when people went to bed, they raked up the fire and made a cross in the ashes, and prayed to God and St Osyth to deliver them from fire and water and from all misadventure.

Strangely enough I could not find the spring, although there is a public pathway round a place called Nun's Wood, which leads down through marshes and glades of knotted oak and willow. I did see, however, when I left the village, a notice warning the motorist to beware of running stags! Then perhaps nothing should surprise me about a village which in its time has introduced the Lombardy poplar and red-legged partridge into England, and has boasted a dragon, many witches, and, of course, a headless saint.

‒ THE WILD MAN OF ORFORD ‒

(A story told by Ralph of Coggeshall, the sixth abbot of Coggeshall Abbey)

It was a grey, grey day; the water and the sky were almost the same colour and a thin ribbon of white mist seemed to be everywhere.

The fishermen, nevertheless, had gone out in their boats. They were not hopeful that they would catch very much, but it would soon be Friday and the villagers would be demanding their fish. It was not an opportunity they could afford to miss.

They tried staying awake but it was difficult when it seemed as though everything around them was drained of colour and life. The nets went down easily enough and then the boat stated to rock – and there was something so large caught in the net that it seemed to almost rip its way out. It took all four of the men to haul this amazing catch. Could it be a whale? Surely not!

Whatever it was, it was struggling so much that it was totally entangled in the net. In desperation, the men took their knives and cut it loose. They half expected it to jump back into the water, but its exertions had left it so exhausted that it just lay still in the bottom of the boat. And finally they could see what it was. It was a man, a great hairy man, and in the matt of hair that covered his chest were shells and sand and other debris of the deep. The hair on his head was torn and battered; the hair on his stomach was shaggy and bristly. He looked fearful. His eyes rolled and all he could do was grunt. Even when the men spoke to him gently, he just shook his head and could say no words.

The men all turned to look at Matthew, the oldest fisherman, to see if he could explain what they had caught. Matthew had never seen anything like it. All he could suggest was that they take the hairy creature to the castle to see if the Lord de Granville would know what it was.

They did not reach the shore until dusk, when a thin sliver of moon was visible. Two of them dragged the man between them with his arms flung over their shoulders. He was not attempting to walk, which made him a heavy load. Seawater was still pouring down his body in rivulets. The path up to the castle was long and steep, so the men took it in turns to drag their catch.

At last they reached the great hall. The noise of people eating meant that the diners were scarcely aware of the door opening. It was the blushing faces of the girls, as they caught sight of the naked man, that first alerted the people to the new arrival. The lord was munching grapes and waved the party into the centre of the room so they could be seen more clearly by the light of the fire.

The lady of the house was throwing titbits to the hounds. She caught sight of the creature's hungry look and waved for him to help himself to food from the table. He ignored the splendid haunches of venison and the slices of ham and instead picked an uncooked fish off a plate. He tore the raw flesh greedily with his bare hands and squashed it into his mouth until juices began to flow down his chin. People moved away from him in disgust. The lord announced, 'I think this is no Christian creature. Take him to the dungeon and in the morning the priest will deal with him.'

In the morning they took him to church. It was obvious that he did not know the significance of the cross on the altar. He neither knelt nor bent his head, and could not speak a single word to praise God. They thought him no better than an animal, so they put him in a cage and hung him upside down. Children came and ran sticks across the iron bars to annoy him.

Then one day the fishermen came back and decided to return him to the water – but with three nets around him so he could not get away. They wanted to see if he could swim. They could not, and thought that anybody who could was in league with the Devil.

As soon as he was released into the water he swam freely. Even the nets did not stop his progress, as he was able to dive deep into the water and avoid them. On and on he swam in total freedom, until he turned and saw the people waving on the shore. He floated on his back and lifted an arm to wave, with a smile and a look of joy; then he disappeared into the water again. Up and down he bobbed. Then a wave came like a lacy shawl and carried him away, and he lifted his arm again for a final wave before he disappeared. The people came a little closer to see if they could catch a glimpse of him but no, he was back in the world he knew: floating seaweed and fish of all kinds. The watchers were filled with jealousy for this creature who was so totally free and at one with nature.

～ THE LOYAL SACRIFICE ～

Ah! There are times, you know, when troubles come from inside a country as well as outside a country, and sometimes these are the worst. A good example of this is this Civil War we've been having, with Parliament fighting against the King. There's been no worse incident in this war than the siege that's been going in Colchester for seventy-six days. Now look how it's ending. That old villain, that foul Puritan Sir Thomas Fairfax, is demanding £14,000 as a fine from us. Just as well we've got those Dutch and Flemish weavers to pay it, for we common folk have nothing left. Even the common soldiers are getting treated badly by the Parliamentarians. Some are taken out of the city, stripped of much of their clothing, beaten and half-starved and others are being sent to the West Indies as slaves.

And I still have not recovered from what happened last night. They have executed Sir Charles Lucas and Sir George Lisle, two of the bravest of the King's officers! I saw it all happen. See, look at that door and those steps in the wall of the castle. That's where the martyrs emerged from inside the jail in the castle. Sir Charles Lucas was the first to be brought out of his cell. Now, I would say he seemed remarkably composed. He looked about him and spoke out loudly, so that we all heard him. My boy was with me and he clung onto my hand. He was frightened of what we were about to witness. What I actually heard Sir Charles say was, 'I have often faced death in the field and now you shall see, I dare die.' Then he prayed for a moment, lifted his head and he opened his doublet and called, 'I am ready for you, now rebels, do your worst!'

I did not dare look and I hid the boy's face against my chest. He was shivering with fear. I heard the musket fire and there was a long pause. When I looked up, nobody had moved the body. It meant that Sir George could see his dead friend when he came out.

Well, Sir George went straight over to where Sir Charles lay on the ground and knelt to kiss him goodbye. The Parliament men at least let him do that and then they let him speak to his relatives. Brave as a fighting cock, he called for the soldiers to come closer to him. A soldier half smiled. 'I warrant, sir, we'll hit you. You need not be concerned.'

Sir George looked slightly amused and shrugged his shoulders. 'I have been nearer to you when you have missed me.' Then he prayed, lifted his head, and looked directly at the soldiers and, like his friend, he said, 'Do your worst.' They did.

There was silence for some time after that. Nobody quite knew what to do or say. Just one old woman muttered that grass would never grow where they fell. We understood what she meant. I told the boy, 'Barren ground always marks an unjust grave. You wait and see. There'll always be a bald patch of grass there.'

~ LOST AT SEA ~

In the house in Wales I lived in as a child, we had a painting in our attic that showed a pretty young woman holding up a baby to look at a portrait of a bearded sailor. I had thought it attractive, until I read the inscription underneath: 'Lost at Sea'. 'Oh, not another slice of Victorian melodrama!' I muttered to myself. Then as an adult I came across something in the old church in Brightlingsea that made me understand the dreadful hazards faced by nineteenth-century seamen.

If you look closely at the walls around the nave of the church, you will see a frieze of Victorian-style tiles. Each tile is the same size and the same design, recording just one mariner's name, his age and details of his death. It was a scheme begun by the vicar Arthur Pertwee in 1872, and continued after his death until 1988. His purpose had been to set up a memorial to sailors who died at sea and could not be buried on land because their bodies had not been recovered.

The bulk of the tiles tell similar stories of the dreadful storms in late Victorian times that destroyed so many smacks. Fathers were often drowned with their teenage sons. And, in a typical example, in the storms of 1883 five smacks and thirty-four men were lost at sea. The tiles record an amazing number of stories that seem to be almost a summary of recent maritime history: Sidney Siebert, who drowned on the *Titanic*; crews who perished off yachts in many parts of the world; losses in both World Wars; and a young sailor knifed by a drunken cook.

Canon Pertwee was only too aware of the dangers faced by men sailing the North Sea in the winter in the frail fishing smacks. On wild winter nights, he would even climb up the church tower and set up a light to guide the ships home. In his parish magazine he would give the full story of the disasters that were recorded on the tiles, especially when the sailor had been a young man leaving behind a widow and children.

To give you an idea of what so frequently happened, I will tell you the story of John Britton. On 11 October 1884 the *Two Sisters* was out in the North Sea. In the morning the weather had been moderate and the sun shone brightly, with only a few big waves showing. The vessel was hove to. At about one o'clock, Britton, not feeling very well, went up on deck, leaving the rest of the crew below.

The skipper, who was busy with preparations for dinner, was vaguely aware that the weather was turning nasty. Then there was a crash louder than the loudest clap of thunder. A tremendous wave struck the vessel and poured a torrent of water down into the cabin. It was two or three minutes before the skipper and the rest of the watch below could scramble up on deck because of the rush of water coming towards them. The vessel was lying on her beam ends.

'Where's Britton?'

Nobody seemed to know. Then one of the men looked over the quarter and saw the poor fellow struggling in the water, some fifty yards astern, his inflated oilskin clothes buoying him up, although he was no swimmer. For five minutes or more, as it seemed, he was visible; but it was impossible to help him, for the rowing boat had been so jammed by the force of the sea between the pinnacle and the quarter that it could not be moved.

'Oh skipper, he's going!' one of the men screamed.

The crew saw him sink before their very eyes. Some tried to shout a tearful 'goodbye!' but the wind took their voices away.

Britton was twenty-six years old – deservedly much loved by his friends and generally respected. Poor young man, he had only been married about fourteen months earlier. Poignantly his wife gave birth to their first baby just before the news of his death arrived. In fact, for some days it was thought wise to withhold the news from her, but eventually the heartrending news was broken to the young widow. There was to be some comfort for the poor girl. The news must have reached the national newspapers, for a London omnibus driver told some of his passengers about the incident. They were so moved that a subscription was immediately raised among them for the benefit of the widow; the amount collected was £5, a considerable sum in those days.

It's well worth paying a visit to the tiles in that church. I only wish similar respect had been paid to the mariners who perished from the village of Borth where I was born in Wales. My great-grandfather drowned in the schooner he captained off the West Indies.

~ THE BATTLE OF THE FLAGS ~

They always say that if you want to find out what happens in a
town, talk to the old man sitting in the graveyard. That's exactly
what I discovered the day I tried to find out the story of the
controversial priest who was the vicar of Thaxted between 1910
and 1942.

I arrived in the town expecting the church to be hidden from
view around the corner of a twisting medieval lane. Indeed, there
were lovely half-timbered houses down the sloping streets and a
splendid twisted Guildhall, but the church's buttressed steeple
stood high on a hill dominating everything around it. They say
the spire is 181ft high, so it was easy to see, even some distance
away. And I found an old man sitting in the graveyard among
the fallen golden leaves. Joy of joys, the old man remembered
the priest!

'Never been another vicar like Conrad Noel in this town and
won't be again, I shouldn't think. He changed the life of this town
for good and for the better I would say, although not everyone
would agree.'

He guided me up to the door of the church and, as soon as I
walked in, I was enthralled. Thaxted Church is without doubt
one of the most stunningly beautiful churches in England. It has
a spaciousness and grace that even some of our bigger cathedrals
lack. The old man saw my expression and smiled.

'He helped make it like this, you know. The church had some
fine medieval craftsmanship, but it didn't show until he got rid of
those musty hangings, not to mention the moth-eaten kneelers
and the Bible boxes. Somehow he made the chancel seem wider
and the seating more flexible, but there were always problems and
arguments with the Establishment. Some didn't like him getting
rid of the padded Bible boxes which many of the gentry used to

use to reserve places for themselves. He was a socialist, you see. He wanted seats to be open to everyone. Amazing really he was so keen in keeping everything so equal, for his family were titled and in royal service – aunt a lady in waiting to the Queen and his father a groom to the privy chamber. His proper name was Conrad Le Despencer Roden Noel. This never put people off. He was liked by the young, the low-paid and the poor, the farm workers, the workers at Lee's sweet factory and the more learned, not to mention Daisy, Duchess of Warwick.

'I always liked what he called his People's Procession, when the Congregation were invited to join in behind the ministers and the servers. There they all were, carrying their banners, lights and flowers – a proper picture! And as for music, we had the famous composer Gustav Holst in charge!' He paused a moment, waiting for me to be suitably impressed. 'Then Mrs Noel she brought in the morris dancers. Now there's life and colour for you and they still come here at certain times of the year.'

'Yes. I am sorry to have missed them.' I walked up the aisle to gaze at the colourful banners that hung in front of the altar. They seemed rather a theatrical touch, as though they had been left after some medieval joust. It was then the old man told me about the battle of the flags.

'During the First World War the vicar had hung the flags of the allies, the red flag and the Sinn Fein flag, and they stayed there after the war. Then you remember, in 1921, there was a miner's strike and someone took the red flag down. That was the signal many people were waiting for to express their discontent with the vicar's radical views. First Cambridge undergraduates came and this time took both the red flag and the Sinn Fein flag down and delivered them by motorcycle to the bishop of Chelmsford.

'Then an Empire Day meeting was to be held. Red, white

and blue bunting was exhibited all over Thaxted. People were encouraged to fly the Union Jack as the flag of freedom. This, it was said, "was the flag for which our boys fought and died". There were shouts of "No Bolshevism for Thaxted, a British town. Loyal citizens fly the true flag". Obviously this created all sorts of tension. Noel supporters pulled down the Union Jacks. Undergraduates pulled down the red flag. There were incidents of both flags being burnt at the bullring. Made things very nasty. The church was shut for four days and there were no more public meetings so things could cool down.

'The chairman of the parish council spoke out against the vicar's political activities. The matter was even taken to the Houses of Parliament, where the Home Office said the vicar had not used language calculated to incite violence, so no action could be taken by the government. Well, in the end, it was a Church Consistory Court who ordered the removal of the red flag and the Sinn Fein flag. Didn't stop the vicar, as you can imagine. Up he goes to the pulpit and declares, "The flag has been removed, but the preaching will go on."'

I turned to look at the bronze bust of Conrad Noel in the church, but somehow it does not show the fire of the man. The old man agreed with me and sent me to see the painting of him in the Guildhall. It was a full-length painting by a British artist called Frank William Carter. Here was a man standing hand on a hip, with a Bible in one hand, fully prepared to face the world and fight for his ideals of justice and for the creation of a 'fragrant shrine of God'. This was a true warrior of Essex, a man in love with her traditions!

⟶ THE KNOWING CAT OF CANVEY ⟵

On Canvey Island, two old men shared a house. One old man was a Christian. The other old man was agnostic. The Christian gentleman said that if he died first he would find a way to come back and convince his friend that there was an afterlife. Sure enough, he did die first.

Later, there was a fierce storm and a knocking. The agnostic gentleman went to the door and opened it. The wind came roaring in but there was nothing to be seen. The weather calmed down and the cat (who had followed the man to the door) started to purr and rub itself against something it both saw and felt. Still the agnostic old man saw nothing, but the cat knew as cats always know! The cat knew who was there.

⟶ THE PHILOSOPHER AT BRIGHTLINGSEA ⟵

John Selleto was dying. Here was a man who had always claimed to be an atheist and this troubled his friends. They tried very hard to persuade him to declare that he had a belief in God, but he would not have it. Eventually their pleas made him turn his face from the pillow with a strange twisted smile, and he said, 'When I am buried, if God exists, an ash tree will grow from my grave.'

His friends thought this was just another of his quirky sayings, yet a few years later the stonework of his tomb at All Saints' Church in Brightlingsea was displaced by an ash sapling growing through it. In time it grew to be a very strong tree, and after 170 years the tree had to be uprooted and the tomb rebuilt.

BIBLIOGRAPHY

These are the books I found most helpful in compiling these stories:

Andrews, William, *Bygone Essex* (1892)

Baring-Gould, Sabine, *Mehalah* (1880)

Barnes, Alison, *Essex Eccentrics* (2004)

Barnes, Alison (ed.), *The Flying Serpent* (1669)

Bax, Clifford, *Highways and Byways in Essex* (1939)

Beckett, R.A., *Romantic Essex* (1902)

Bowman, Karen, *Essex Girls* (2010)

Brooks, Pamela, *Essex Ghosts and Legends* (2010)

Carter, Douglas, *Boxted: Portrait of an English Village* (2006)

Crossley-Holland, Kevin, *British Folk Tales* (1987)

Cubbin, Sue, *That Precious Legacy: Ralph Vaughan Williams and Essex Folksong* (2006)

Gaskill, Malcolm, *Witchfinders: A Seventeenth-Century English Tragedy* (2005)

Grey, Adrian, *Tales of Old Essex* (1987)

Hendy, Phyl, *The St Osyth Witch Story* (1993)

Howlett, Sue, *The Secrets of the Mound: Mersea Barrow 1912-2012* (2012)

Kent, Sylvia, *Folklore of Essex* (2005)

Lovell, Keith, *In the Land of the Tolles* (1991)

Morgan, Glyn, *Secret Essex* (1982)

Morton, Carl, *How Green is our Village* (1976)

Payne, Jessie, *A Ghost Hunter's Guide to Essex* (1987)

Pitt-Stanley, Sheila, *Legends of Leigh* (1989)

Puttick, Betty, *Ghosts of Essex* (1997)

Sharpe, James, *The Myth of the English Highwayman* (2010)

Simpson, Jacqueline, *British Dragons* (1980)

Smith, Graham, *Smuggling in Essex* (2005)

Summers, Andrew and Debenham, John *The Essex Hundred: Histories* (2008)

Twinch, Carol, *Essential Essex* (2009)

Wakeling, Alfred and Moon, Peter, *Tiles of Tragedy* (2001)

Westwood, Jennifer and Simpson, Jacqueline, *The Lore of the Land: A Guide to England's Legends* (2005)

Yearsley, Ian, *Islands of Essex* (2000)

Other:

Thaxted Bulletin, Issue No. 85, spring edition (2010)

If you enjoyed this book, you may also be interested in ...

Essex Villains: Rogues, Rascals & Reprobates
PAUL WREYFORD

Essex can boast some of the country's most notorious figures. The legendary Dick Turpin was Essex born and bred, and in Manningtree the ruthless Matthew Hopkins scoured the area in search of 'witches' – putting to death anyone who had as much as a wart on the end of their nose. Even royalty have carried out dastardly deeds within the county's borders.

978 0 7524 6574 6

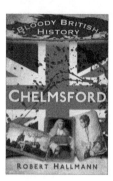

Bloody British History: Chelmsford
ROBERT HALLMANN

Chelmsford has one of the darkest histories on record. From the skeletons lying underneath the city – which include a woolly mammoth – to the executions of thieves, witches, martyrs and murderers at Chelmsford's gaol, this book will change the way you see the town forever.

978 0 7524 7115 0

Haunted Chelmsford
JASON DAY

Much of the more sinister history of England took place in Chelmsford and it would seem that many of the participants – and victims – of these events still haunt the town today. Join Jason Day as he introduces you to the ghost of an anguished nun, a phantom technician at the Civic Theatre, and a spectral cyclist. Encounter the 'Box Monster' and the spirits of women falsely accused of witchcraft. Dare you read on?

978 0 7524 6221 9